# Men, Mines And Memories
## IRON MINING IN IRON COUNTY, MICHIGAN

PUBLISHED BY
IRON COUNTY MUSEUM
P.O. BOX 272, CASPIAN, MICHIGAN 49915

ISBN 0-9677230 - 1 - 9
Library Congress No. 2001 132831
Copyright: Iron County Museum, 2001

EDITOR: MARCIA BERNHARDT
INTERVIEWERS: HAROLD BERNHARDT
DEBRA BERNHARDT

Printed by
HAHN PRINTING, INC.
Eagle River, Wisconsin 54521

# ACKNOWLEDGMENTS

Special thanks to those individuals who loaned photos and consented to be interviewed, to Harold and Debra Bernhardt for interviewing, to the Iron County Museum for use of its extensive archival collection of mining materials and photographs, to the Harbour House Museum for additional photographs, to the many Museum volunteers who perused and marked local newspapers for recording material about local mining and who assisted with tabulating the names of those who lost their lives from Mining Inspector Reports, to other researchers - - particularly Vivian Fredlund, Dr. Allen Johnson and Harry Colony, to Shirley Deroche for transcribing and typing, and to Nora Kneebone and Eva Noteboom for assistance with layouts and final copy preparation. Lastly, thanks to the Michigan Humanities Council for funding to do the final research and preparation for this publication.

MB

**The Cover:** It is a reprint of a painting by the late Douglas McGreaham (1960-1981) son of Charles and Mitzie McGreaham. Doug loved Iron County and was a proponent of preserving its history and culture. A talented young artist about to complete his degree, he lost his life in service to the University of Michigan.

**DEDICATED TO**

Those who lost their lives in the mines and
also those who toiled for their livelihood in them as well

Lastly, to our daughter, the late
Debra Bernhardt
Who during her brief life felt compelled to
record accounts of "Ordinary People"

## TABLE OF CONTENTS

# MINING IN IRON COUNTY, MICHIGAN

## The Beginning

In <u>A History of Iron County</u> author, Jack Hill, mentions the 1851 iron ore discovery in Stambaugh by surveyor, Harvey Mellon. Earlier, William H. Selden, in an address to the Upper Peninsula Branch of the Michigan Pioneer and Historical Society in 1925, referred to Mellon's 1847 notes indicating the discovery of iron deposits.

By 1875 prospectors began taking numerous excursions into Iron County. John Armstrong is credited with the discovery of the first merchantable ores near the falls of the Paint River, later to become the Crystal Falls Mine, which shipped 1.241 tons prior to the arrival of the railroad in 1882.

Edward Breitung opened the Mastodon Mine in Alpha in 1881 and the following year shipped 3,477 Tons. Additional mines opened in each county community. Doctor D.M. Bond developed a mine in Mansfield, Donald MacKinnon discovered ore in Spring Valley—now Caspian-Gaastra; the Seldens, William and Richard, in Stambaugh; the MacKinnon Brothers, Alexander, Donald and Archie in Iron River. Stambaugh exploration began in 1879, the same year as Iron River. First ore was shipped upon the arrival of the railroad in 1882. Total shipping for the year was 31,595 tons from the Iron River-Stambaugh mines as compared to 42,111 tons from the Crystal Falls area.

The first mining machinery was brought to the Iron River Mine in Stambaugh by the Iron River Mining Company. Machinery consisted of a small upright boiler and hoist, both of which were brought from Florence, Wisconsin by stone boats drawn by horses and mules.

Iron mining was undeniably the major part of the economy of Iron County for nearly 100 years, with mines operating from 1881 to 1978 and the last ore shipped in 1979. It is difficult to establish the exact number of mining explorations and/or mines in Iron County. In the unpublished research of Vivian Fredlund, 127 explorations are listed. Further, Fredlund identifies 79 mines, which shipped 208,345,852 tons of ore between 1882 and 1967.

In a mine subsidence and water drainage study by Dr. Allen M. Johnson and Professor Gordon Franlli of Michigan Technological University in 1976, 55 separate mining operations are noted for the West Iron County area with total shipping, 147,019,638 tons. This was followed by a study in 1983 of East Iron County Mines by Johnson and Lawrence J. Mac Donald in which some 45-52 mines were identified and 58,727,872 tons were recorded.

To be more exact is difficult since mines often were known by different names in different periods of time or they may have been absorbed into another mine because of shipping and so one finds major groupings rather than individual mines.

Tragedies are a part of Iron County Mining history and have been noted in both Mansfield and Amasa when large numbers of men were killed at one time. In the book <u>Black Rock and Roses</u>, comprised of some 100 interviews, the author says, "Books don't tell the life. Come with me to hear the voices of a hundred grandfathers and mothers—your neighbors perhaps, as they pump blood into the past of Iron County." By count, 562 deaths have been identified in the period of 100 years in the mining industry.

# LIST OF MINING COMPANIES

This list of mining companies, which have operated in Iron County may be incomplete. It was assembled from the Iron Mining Inspectors' Reports and all are not available. Names of companies, operating prior to the establishment of that office in 1889, were obtained from the book, **A History of Iron County**, by Jack Hill.

American-Boston Mining Co.
Balkan Mining Co.
Bates Iron Co.
Bird Iron Co.
Briar Hill Mining Co. 1882
Buffalo Iron Mining Co.
Bristol Mining Co.
Brule Mining Co.
Calidonia Co.
Cleveland Cliffs Iron Co.
Cleveland Iron Co.
Corrigan McKinney and Co.
Corrigan McKinney Steel Co.
Crystal Falls Iron Co. 1880
Cuyahoga Mining Co.
Davidson Ore Mining Co.
Delta Mining Co.
DeSota Iron Mining Co.
Emmet Mining Co. 1881
Florence Iron Co.
Florence-Iron River Mining Co.
Fortune Lake Mining Co.
G.W. Youngs Mining Co.
Hanna Coal and Ore Corp.
Hanna Furnace Co.
Hanna Iron Ore Co.
Hanna (M.A.) Co.
Hemlock River Mining Co.
Hewitt Mining Co. (Furnace Co.)
Hollister Mining Co.
Hope Iron Mining Co.
Huron Iron Mining Co.

Iron River Mining Co.
Inland Steel Co.
James Mining Co.
Judson Mining Co.
Jones and Laughlin Ore Co.
Jones and Laughlin Steel Corp.
Mansfield Iron Mining Co.
Mastodon Iron Co.
McDonald Mining Co.
Metropolitan Iron Co.
Mineral Mining Co.
Mineral Hills Mining Co.
Monroe (Munro) Iron Mining Co. 1907
Nanaimo Mining Co. 1881
Newman Ore Co.
Nevada Mining Co.
North Range Mining Co.
Oglebay, Norton and Co.
Oliver Iron Mining Co.
Pickands Mather and Co.
Pickands Mining Co.
Pittsburgh Coke and Iron Co.
Republic Steel Corp.
Roberts Ore Co.
Rogers-Brown Ore Co.
Thropp, T.E.
Todd Stambaugh Co.
Verona Mining Co.
Victor Schlitz Mining Co. 1899
Wickwire Mining Co.
Youngstown Mines Corp.

# LIST OF MINES THAT SHIPPED ORE IN IRON COUNTY 1882-1978

| NAME OF MINE | LOCATION | PRODUCTION YEARS | TONNAGE PRODUCED | TOTAL INCLUDING COMBINED PRODUCT TONNAGE |
|---|---|---|---|---|
| 1. Alpha | Crystal Falls | 1903 | 1,380 | 1,370 |
| 2. Armenia | Crystal Falls | 1889-1914 | 713,395 | 713,395 |
| 3. Baker | Stambaugh | 1909-1915 | 267,107 | 267,107 |
| 4. Balkan-Judson | Alpha | 1917-1942 | 3,994,484 | 4,441,799  Includes Mastodon |
| 5. Bates | Iron River | 1915-1947 | 4,054,666 | 4,054,666 |
| 6. BengalTully-Cannon | Stambaugh | 1913-1963 | 5,671,823 | 11,621,703  Includes Tully-Cannon |
| 7. Berkshire | Caspian | 1908-1950 | 4,189,586 | Included Buck Total |
| 8. Beta | Iron River | 1886-1942 | 27,156 | 27,156 |
| 9. Book | Alpha | 1943-1957 | 2,205,055 | 2,205,055 |
| 10. Bristol-Youngstown | Crystal Falls | 1890-1969 | 18,713,186 | 18,713,186 |
| 11. Brule | Stambaugh | 1936 | 4,200 | 4,200 |
| 12. Baltic | Caspian | 1901-1950 | 2,574,216 | Included Buck Total |
| 13. Buck-Buck Group | Caspian | 1901-1967 | 5,412,657 | 21,098,287  Includes Baltic, Berkshire, Fogarty, Zimmerman & Degrasse |
| 14. Cardiff | Iron River | 1922-1923 | 144,415 | Included Homer Total |
| 15. Carpenter | Crystal Falls | 1914-1928 | 2,735,452 | 2,735,452 |
| 16. Caspian | Caspian | 1903-1937 | 6,623,320 | 6,623,320 |
| 17. Cayia | Crystal Falls | 1953 | 44,492 | 44,492 |
| 18. Cannon | Stambaugh | 1952-1963 | 4,796,663 | Included Bengal-Tully Total |
| 19. Chatham | Stambaugh | 1907-1920 | 1,381,175 | Included Hiawatha # 1 Total |
| 20. Chicagon | Iron River | 1911-1922 | 1,234,339 | 1,234,339 |
| 21. Columbia | Crystal Falls | 1882-1950 | 4,308,601 | 4,308,601 |
| 22. Corry "40" | Stambaugh | 1922-1928 | 67,616 | Included Berkshire Total |
| 23. Cortland | Stambaugh | 1912-1914 | 52,148 | 52,148 |
| 24. Cottrell | Caspian | 1915-1916 | 75,134 | 75,134 |
| 25. Crystal Falls | Crystal Falls | 1882-1913 | 1,744,015 | 1,744,015 |
| 26. Delphic | Alpha | 1883-1896 | 33,770 | 33,770 |
| 27. Davidson Group 1,2,3 | Iron River | 1911-1953 | 8,197,014 | 8,197,014 |
| 28. Davidson # 4 | Iron River | 1913-1921 | 128,599 | 128,599 |
| 29. Degrasse | Gaastra | 1950 | 2 8,682 | Included Buck Group Total |
| 30. Delta | Iron River | 1920-1925 | 95,759 | 95,759 |
| 31. Dunn | Crystal Falls | 1887-1915 | 2,208,511 | 2,208,511 |
| 32. Fogarty | Caspian | 1907-1949 | 1,515,721 | Included Buck Group Total |
| 33. Forbes | Iron River | 1913-1946 | 2,283,822 | 2,283,822 |
| 34. Fortune Lake | Crystal Falls | 1953-1956 | 1,175,341 | 1,175,341 |
| 35. Genesse | Crystal Falls | 1902-1935 | 1,198,383 | 1,198,383 |
| 36. Gibson | Amasa | 1885-1911 | 159,453 | 159,453 |
| 37. Great Western | Crystal Falls | 1882-1925 | 2,296,739 | 2,296,739 |
| 38. Half & Half | Unknown | 1889-1891 | 7,524 | 7,524 |
| 39. Hemlock | Amasa | 1891-1938 | 2,125,756 | 2,125,756 |
| 40. Hersel | Unknown | 1890 | 955 | 955 |
| 41. Hiawatha # 1 | Stambaugh | 1893-1950 | 8,502,729 | 9,883,904  Includes Chatham |
| 42. Hiawatha # 2 | Caspian | 1935-1966 | 12,294,722 | 12,294,722 |
| 43. Hilltop | Crystal Falls | 1899-1919 | 98,202 | 98,202 |
| 44. Hollister | Crystal Falls | 1890-1914 | 43,117 | 43,117 |
| 45. Hope | Crystal Falls | 1892-1903 | 28,530 | 28,530 |
| 46. Homer | Iron River | 1915-1969 | 16,515,753 | 16,660,168  Includes Cardiff |
| 47. James (Osana) | Iron River | 1907-1953 | 8,329,598 | 8,329,598 |
| 48. Kimball | Crystal Falls | 1907-1915 | 35,757 | 35,757 |
| 49. Lamont (Monitor) | Crystal Falls | 1889-1910 | 558,524 | 558,524 |
| 50. Lawrence | Crystal Falls | 1920-1956 | 6,693 | 6,693 |
| 51. Le Peck | Crystal Falls | 1892 | 2,844 | 2,844 |
| 52. Lincoln | Crystal Falls | 1891-1909 | 241,627 | 241,627 |
| 53. Mansfield | Crystal Falls | 1890-1913 | 1,462,504 | 1,462,504 |
| 54. Mastodon | Alpha | 1882-1942 | 447,315 | 447,315  Included Balkan-Judson Total |
| 55. McDonald | Crystal Falls | 1909-1913 | 30,289 | 30,289 |
| 56. Michigan | Amasa | 1893-1916 | 350,270 | 350,270 |
| 57. Monogahela | Crystal Falls | 1901-1943 | 1,352,591 | 1,352,591 |
| 58. Nanaimo | Iron River | 1882-1908 | 373,765 | 373,765 |
| 59. Odgers | Crystal Falls | 1916-1935 | 2,101,381 | 2,101,381 |
| 60. Porter | Amasa | 1916-1927 | 733,327 | 733,327 |
| 61. Paint River | Crystal Falls | 1882-1913 | 382,078 | 382,078 |
| 62. Perry | Unknown | 1883 | 3,138 | 3,138 |
| 63. Ravenna-Prickett | Crystal Falls | 1911-1943 | 635,227 | 635,227 |
| 64. Richards | Crystal Falls | 1913-1927 | 534,448 | 534,448 |
| 65. Riverton Group | Iron River | 1882-1937 | 5,881,550 | 5,881,550 |
| 66. Rodgers | Iron River | 1914-1945 | 2,907,375 | 2,907,375 |
| 67. Sheridan | Iron River | 1899-1900 | 116,299 | 116,299 |
| 68. South Mastodon | Alpha | 1887-1890 | 8,203 | 8,203 |
| 69. Spies-Virgil | Iron River | 1912-1956 | 2,145,965 Spies  2,049,146 Virgil | 4,195,111 |
| 70. Sherwood | Iron River | 1931-1978 | 13,713,067 | 1 3,713,067 |
| 71. Tobin | Crystal Falls | 1905-1962 | 6,663,694 | 6,663,694 |
| 72. Tully | Stambaugh | 1910-1950 | 1,153,217 | Included Bengal-Tully-Cannon |
| 73. Youngs | Gaastra | 1905-1928 | 802,751 | 802,751 |
| 74. Youngstown | Crystal Falls | 1882-1897 | 151,425 | 151,425 |
| 75. Wickwire | Iron River | 1911-1917 | 128,869 | 128,869 |
| 76. Wauseca_Aronson | Iron River | 1926-1968 | 14,822,826 | 14,822,826 |
| 77. Warner | Amasa | 1915-1957 | 2,834,927 | 2,834,027 |
| 78. Zimmerman | Gaastra | 1907-1950 | 3,609,727 | Included Buck Group Total |

Total  208,345,852

# MINING INSPECTION

To describe what is included in a mining inspector's annual report, each report includes information about each working mine. Mines are alphabetized and individual reports include tons of ore mined, tons shipped, average number of men employed, number and description of every accident, and also the fatalities. Charts are included giving lists of operating companies, names of area mining superintendents, individual mine superintendents, mine captains, and respective addresses of each. Charts also classify and total accidents. Fatal accidents are described. Some reports also include policies, rules, and drawings.

## LIST OF MINING INSPECTORS

| | | | |
|---|---|---|---|
| Pre-1900 | A. Gulgren | 1938-1944 | Frank J. Carlson |
| 1900-1909 | John Worden | 1944-1946 | William Melchiori |
| 1909-1912 | William Carlson | 1946-1948 | Frank J. Carlson |
| 1912-1918 (?) | W.H. Jobe | 1948-1958 | William Melchiori |
| 1918-1920 | Fred Mitchell | 1958-1973 | Reino Anderson |
| 1920-1921 | Frank Comienski | 1959-1965 | Deputy: Joseph Lalande |
| 1922-1928 | Daniel J. Watts | 1962-1965 | Assistant: Hugo Riverside |
| 1928-1934 | Charles Richards | 1974-1975 | Mervin Mylchreest |
| 1934-1936 | Frank J. Carlson | 1976-1979 | Mario Contardi |
| 1936-1938 | Gust J. Peterson | 1980-2001 | Peter Korach |

## ANNUAL REPORT OF WILLIAM CARLSON, INSPECTOR OF MINES
### From Sept. 30, 1911 to Sept. 30, 1912

To the Honorable Board of Supervisors of Iron County, State of Michigan:

Gentleman—I have the honor to submit herewith my annual report for the year ending September 30 as follows:

Table No 1— Gives the names of mines, shows output, men employed and number of accidents.

Table No. 2—Shows mines, locations, officials and P.O. Addresses.

Table No. 3—Shows mining companies operating in Iron County, the Superintendents and number of men employed.

Table No. 4—Shows record of accidents.

Table No. 5—Shows table of summaries.

## ANNUAL REPORT OF DANIEL J. WATTS, MINING INSPECTOR
### For year ending September 30, 1923

During the period covered in this report one hundred and ninety-six (196) underground inspections were made at the thirty (30) active mines of the county.

In addition to the underground inspections, frequent inspections were made on surface of all equipment, open pits, and so on. Many openings were found that were not adequately guarded. These have been fairly well cared for now and we expect to give this further attention in the future.

I have had some difficulty in persuading certain mining companies to follow out my orders and in many instances unnecessary delay was experienced. I am glad to report that such companies are greatly in the minority and that in most cases I found ready and hearty cooperation from the superintendents.

According to the degree that superintendents consider safety first work imperative and important, I find that certain mines are more seriously engaged in safeguarding their employees, and are providing maximum safety by employing modern safety devices, warning signs, safety activities and operations. Because of these measures, the report this year indicates a noted and gratifying reduction in accidents, despite the fact that mines have been operated at near normal capacity all summer. This fact, I am sure, will be pleasing and of intense interest to all mining men and others concerned about the occupation of mining.

## REPORT OF REINO ANDERSON, INSPECTOR OF MINES 1958-1973

I began working as mine inspector in 1959, January the 1st, and a few months later, I had my first disaster. I had a local mine (the Sherwood) in Iron River, where six men were killed by steam—there was a pool of water laying on top surface which broke through. In fact on the West side mines, we had a lot of slate fires, not a fire that is flaming. It is like a coke fire—slates get real hot when exposed to oxygen—that's from sulfur, and this water was so heavy it finally found its way to the sulfur bed that was burning and it created such a steam—over 1000 degrees F. and it just went on their ventilation tract and whatever was in their road—it just scalded them—burnt them, and we lost six men on that accident. That was my worst disaster.

Before, in the olden days, miners wore soft hats, and they weren't compelled to wear safety goggles, or hard toed boots or shoes—all that is a new safety factor which saves a lot of eyes. We used to have numerous amount of eye accidents—in the last ten years that I was an inspector, we had very seldom an eye injury unless somebody violated.

The unions played a big part, but I think the companies also, because you can't give the credit only to the unions because the insurance, the disability was costing the company a lot of money. So they thought they better do something about the safety measures. They were very good about taking our recommendations. We never had any trouble with the mine companies. In the olden days they never kept the names of the fellows that got killed. They were mostly young fellows from Europe that came over here. . . To look at the past records of the mining inspectors, they just said "so many Swedes, so many Finns, so many Polish, so many Italians" . . .They didn't have cages in them days, they had them ride the skip—the same bucket that they hoisted the dirt with and the guys who were daring, the young fellows before they got to the level where they get off, they jumped and missed and then fell down the shafts . . . They didn't even have funeral pay. The party had to pay for their own funeral bills.

The labor unions came in here in the late 30's. They tried hard before, but anytime the officials heard of it, they made it real mean for the men. They didn't want this to come in, but it finally did come in—in the 40's –and I think it was better for the companies because they didn't have to deal with all the men in the mines, they only dealt with a small group . . . It was easier to deal with three or four men than 100 men, and I think this is why they accepted it.

There were attempts to organize before the 30's. I remember when my dad was in the mines, they had secret meetings at night and they were sure that nobody would find out about it. They were trying to organize, but it never took hold. It was The Industrial Workers of the World—IWW. In the early years, I think they were all scared for their jobs. They wouldn't do anything that would sacrifice their jobs.

Mining officials got into politics like school boards, city commissions and stuff like that. I think the big reason in the early days was because the cities had a little higher tax than the townships, and they drew their own boundary lines . . . They tried to keep them in the townships because the tax was cheaper.

# DIAMOND DRILLING

### HERB EDWARDS--*Diamond Driller*

I came to Amasa in 1901 and left again in 1905 or 1906 until about 1912. I made a trip around the world. I ran diamond drill down in the Philippine Islands for two years. We went out by way of the Pacific and after we got through, came home through the Suez, through Europe. You could make that now in about two days, but all you'd see is clouds.

My dad was a mining captain. He had charge of a couple mines on the Mesabi Range. He was a Welshman, born and raised.

In 1906, I was on the Dober property diamond drilling. There was no Caspian at that time. They had found ore there. There was quicksand. They were putting it down and the shaft was all twisted out of shape. They straightened it up again afterward.

I went to work helping on the drill. After I'd helped a little while, I go a job running. The first job I had running was north of Iron River at Morrison Creek, about seven miles north of Iron River and nine miles from Amasa. I used to come home sometimes on Saturdays when my folks was here and go back on Sunday. After that we drilled over in Bates Township, before the Rogers Mine was in there. I worked for the Longyear and Hodge Diamond Drilling Company. Since Odgers quit there hasn't been any diamond drill company in Iron County.

I can remember when I worked over there at the Virgil Mine. I was a mechanic, repairing drill machines and pumps. I had to go down in the mine to repair the pumps. They were sinking shaft. They had one pump in the shaft to keep the water down so the guys could work in the bottom. Saturday nights they'd close the pump down about eleven o'clock or so and Sunday afternoon they'd start the pump so the shaft would be dry by morning. I'd have to take the engineer down there to the pump on the level. I'd ride the bucket down to the pump. There'd be about twelve feet of water in there and all there was to stand on was a plank—one for the pump and one to stand on. If you fell off of that plank, you'd be drowned like a rat in that cold water. I wanted a ladder in there. We had a little Cousin Jack Captain, Captain Duff and he said, "There'll be no bloody ladder in that shaft. Any time you blast it'll be busted up . . ." I said, ". . . I'll have the blacksmith do it, hang it in the shaft on a cable. Well, a fella fall off that plank, he hasn't a chance.—That plank was all damp and slippery. . ."

D.B. 1/22/1976

# MINERS' ACCOUNTS

### CLIFFORD GOODMAN--*Sunshine, Tramming and Plumbing*

I was born in Loretto on the bank of the Sturgeon River. We moved all the way from Loretto, Quinnesec, Norway, Crystal Falls, and then Iron River. They called them mining camps. We used to go from place to place.

My dad worked in the mines. In Crystal Falls, I don't know how many mines they was working there, but there was twenty-six saloons on Main Street. Can you believe that? I was a kid then only nine or ten years old.

At the old Crystal Falls mine, I used to give out sunshine balls. Sunshine was the stuff used in a lamp. The lamp looked like a coffee pot hanging from your hat, but smaller. Sunshine came in big balls and you put it in hot water and it would get soft like lard. Then you had a cup and you put it in cold water and it would get hard again. You pry it out and give it to the miners before they went underground. I used to help the old dry men give out these sunshine balls. Candles came first before sunshine. Sunshine—1906, 1907, 1908.

We lived in the old Smith Mine Location. That's all down now. We lived in the Old Hollister mine. My dad worked there before my time. He also worked at the mine in Mansfield and he worked night shift in a stope. A stope is a big hole in the dirt. Sometimes they had all their holes drilled to blast and it was too early to blast, so they were laying on the dirt there. My dad said, "Do you hear something going rrmph, rrrrrmm,rrrrrrrrrrmmm?" He asked his partner, old Jack Jones, "What in the devil is that?" And Jack said, "That's the pine logs rubbin' in the river bed." The rivers were full of logs in them days, pine logs, and the logs were rubbing the bottom of the river. They could hear that through the ground. It was so close to the surface. My dad quit after he heard the logs going through there. He said, "If that's the logs rubbing in the river, I'm not staying here." He quit. I think he said it was only three weeks after that when it broke through and drowned all those men. Twenty-six men and three mules, I guess.

So, at fifteen years old, I went underground at the Carpenter Mine. My dad told the captain and the shift bosses, "You make it as miserable as you can for this young bugger so he'll get out of here." So the Italians would load the wheelbarrows full of iron ore. I only weighed about 115 pounds and I'd wheel that thing out. I had all my knuckles skinned from rubbing on the sides of the small holes. It was too heavy, but I stuck it out.

I started out as a trammer. In the mornings there was a whole bunch of us young guys that were trammers. We'd get off at the top level just like getting off in a twenty story building, and then we'd go down these ladders. The night shift had blasted the drifts/tunnels and there would be big piles of dirt in each place. So we'd hurry up and look and if there was too much dirt we'd go to the next place. When we'd find a small pile of dirt, that's where we'd stay. But when the shift boss come through, he'd say, "What you doing here?" "Oh, I'm working here today." There'd be a big argument. He'd say, "Some of you gotta move. Who was here first?" "Well, I was here first!" They had to split the crew up so they'd get us to go in different places. None of us wanted a big dirt pile. Sometimes it'd take you three, four, five hours. A miner them days was a high-class man. He was considered a somebody. Us trammers weren't. I got $2.85 a day as a trammer.

I worked as a trammer at the Carpenter from 1915-1917 and I went in the Navy. The Carpenter Mine, when Verona took it over, changed the name to the Lawrence, after Charlie Lawrence.

So, when I got home after the war, I started work at the Baltic, but there was a depression in 1921. There wasn't a wheel turning no place. Nobody even had a bite of bread to eat anymore, and I got a job in the Baltic for two dollars and ten cents a day.

I got married and then I worked at the Warner Mine in Amasa. I'd take a train from here to Crystal Falls and then, there was no other way, I rode a bicycle from Crystal to the boarding house in Amasa. I'd work there all week. Then I'd ride the bicycle back to Crystal and catch the train to come and see her (My wife).

Then I took up plumbing and I worked as a plumber for eleven years. When the Inland Steel started up at the Sherwood, it was during the war (WWII) I couldn't get no material whatsoever. Fred Olson couldn't get materials either, so we went to Inland and asked, "Why don't you come up and work for us, so I went up, took my tools and we plumbed them all up and did their piping and got along good. Then when they started sinking shafts, they treated me so good, they gave me a job as hoistman in the engine house. But I was too lonesome. I said, "Give me my old pipe wrenches and let me go outside and work day shift and fix all the pipes." They said, "We need somebody in the shop." So I went in the shop and repaired drill machines and hoses and everything. They had trouble with the pumps, always the pumps. I knew lots about stuff like that, so I stayed right on as pumpman. On Sunday, I would go out any time of the day I felt like it, put in two or three hours, and got paid for a full day. I pleased myself. So, I stayed there till I retired in 1962.

The first time I ever voted, 1921, I voted in Caspian for Billy Jobe. He was superintendent of the Caspian Mine. Up there by the bridge them days there was kegs of beer, one right on top of the other with a big sign on top, "Vote for Billy Jobe." All the miners would come out, stop there with their dinner pails and fill their pails, have a few beers, have a party and don't forget to vote for Billy Jobe.

Some of them guys those days, if you knew how to do it, would vote four or five times. They just changed their names different ways. But all of Billy Jobe's men counted the votes, all the mining company men, the officials would count the votes. Billy Jobe was for the mining companies.

There were rooster fights on Sunday afternoon after church. My dad used to fight roosters and if his rooster licked the captain's rooster, you had to move out of the (company) house.

After unionization, conditions changed one hundred percent. It went too far as far as I'm concerned. Like these union taking all this money now and making the company pay for all kinds of things. The Poor Company, if you got a million or two million dollars sunk in the ground, you ain't got a thing to say about it today…I never belonged to the union, not until the last years I worked at Inland Steel. They forced me to belong to it, see? They put all these pumps on automatic and I was working as a maintenance man.

When my father was working they talked about the I.W.W. and the guys hear you, they squeal on you right away and you were fired. Because we were so scared of that I.W.W., we didn't have nothing to do with it.

(One more tale) Charlie Lawrence was a good old guy. When Superintendent Lawrence was over in Amasa, he wore a big western hat. He was a big man, a beautiful man. There were three saloons in Amasa them days. The old Hemlock mine was running and the Amasa. He was the boss of the whole community. My dad used to go down town and get drunk lots of times. Cousin Jacks them days used to do that. So he'd put up a big sign, "No drinks to Morrie Goodman". Morrie Goodman was my dad. So my dad would go down town and Jack Weakman would be there, Jack the Bat and Billy Daniels, all at the bar, party every night. He'd (Jack or Billy) say to the bartender, "Give me a glass of beer!" The bartender would give it to him and he'd hand it over to my dad. Here, Morrie, this is yours." He'd just take the beer and give it to him. The bartender didn't do it. Lawrence couldn't stop it.

D.B. 1/10/1974

## OSCAR GREENLUND--*Bells and Hoisting*

My folks came from Sweden, but we came up here in the last part of 1882 or the first part of 1883. My dad worked in the mines. In 1893 when I was three years old, times were hard. There wasn't any work in Iron River so my dad took us back to Commonwealth, Wisconsin, where he got work at the Badger mine. We stayed there seven years till 1900 when we moved back to Stambaugh.

The communities around here got started when the mining companies come in—they're the ones that operated this place, each company was on its own. The Tully Mine was the Corrigan Mc Kinney Company. They came in, brought up so much property, built their own houses—built their own location, had their own shift boss and captain. Each company sent out cruisers and found this ore and started on their own.

My dad worked in the Riverton part time and he worked in the Isabella pit right down around that curve at the foot of the hill. That was an open pit at the time. Later on, of course, he worked at the Hiawatha, the Baltic and different mines. In the early days there was no problem getting work. They could quit at one place one day and go to work at another one the next day. If they got a job they didn't like, they would leave. Some of the places were pretty dangerous in the mines. The Riverton had a bad name for being dangerous.

I never got to know the mining game very well although I worked for the Verona for what I would like to call fifty years, but it wasn't actually fifty years because I was gone at different times. I was in the First World War, I think it was fifteen months.

I went to work one day at thirteen years of age. They put me in the mill. I had never been in the mill (stave mill) before and I was scared stiff, belts and pulleys and machines going, big saws. The work wasn't too hard for me. All I did was put staves in the planer, but you had to keep going all the time. I never went back to get my pay for that day.

I was sixteen years old when I went to the Verona Mining Company and got a job at the Fogarty mine. I was there when they sank the shaft at the Fogarty. They were going down from the surface. All the way down I was working on the top, they called us the landers. We sent down timber and when they hoisted we dumped the buckets and pushed it out on the piles. That's where I started in. I worked there about five years.

Everybody was hardworking. Underground they worked hard and they had to shovel the iron ore by hand. They threw it out in the cars and trammed in, out the shaft and sent it up. I don't know what created the purpose, but each crew, each shift, would try to beat the other. At the Baltic there were 350 skips of ore the first night I was there. When one crew got a few more, the other crew tried to tie that up.

When I came back after the war in 1919, they took me back at the Bengal as a hoisting engineer. They were sympathetic because I was a veteran and crippled. I took the cage hoist because I could sit down and run it. The fellas who had taken over our jobs during the war got placed in other jobs and that wasn't always so nice. The Verona ran the Bengal. It was an operating company. There was the Baltic, the Fogarty, the Bengal, and the Zimmerman later on. The last years I spent up at the Zimmerman. I retired in 1956 so I have already had more than sixteen years of retirement.

As hoisting engineer, I had to do the hoisting by the bell system. They were pretty crude. The miners pulled a wire and there would be weights on them. Sometimes when the wire got too heavy for the contraction on top, the bell wouldn't release and you wouldn't get the right number of bells for the signal they meant. And once in a while that long wire would break and the fellows working in the shaft couldn't signal you.

It (the bell) was sort of a triangle and a knocker would hit it. Later on, of course, they got the electric system, so we got the signal through the wires. But then it was all hand signals.

A standard two bells was always to lower with nobody riding. We had a skip on one rope and a cage on the other one. They counteracted. When the skip came up, the cage went down. When they gave you two bells, that meant they were through with the cage or whatever it was.

Three bells was used when they gave the signal to the skiptender to dump dirt in the skip. The hoistman would take it all the way up to the dump. If they wanted to go slow, like when they were pulling up a timber and they would have to go slow until they got out in the shaft hanging straight, they would give you five bells. Four bells would be to lower slow. Six was the signal for men riding to surface. If they wanted to go to a different level, they'd ring once, pause, and the number of rings for the level.

Mining people got into politics, but one thing I remember the townspeople sort of properly resented the mining men running for office. They used that leverage to try to beat them. To my way of thinking, a lot of these men were educated and they were probably more qualified for some of these jobs. It was better for the people that some of them did get elected. I don't think they dominated city politics to any great extent, but to my way of thinking at least. I know during Jobe's series there, he got so he was the one, everything was Republican at that time—there was no party. There probably wasn't more than half a dozen Democrats in the county. But in the later years of Jobe's reign, they run Victor Lang, the superintendent of the Oliver Mining Company, against Jobe. I know he had one of my acquaintances sitting on top of the city hall with a slogan, "Vote for Lang and bust the gang!" They made the elections more spirited in the older days. Lang was elected, by the way.

I ran for treasurer of the township before I went into the army. After I got back, they coaxed me to run again. I probably got sympathy votes. They used that system that after a fella run a couple of years, he would probably get it. It was sort of a plum job. They would get elected and turn the job over to the bank. When I got in, the pay was $1200 a year. Before I got in, they got a percentage of the taxes, probably about $2400 a year, but they changed it the year I got elected. Like I said, it was a plum job because I had my regular job at the same time.

D.B. 5/1973

# JAMES BORNS--*Tramming and Drilling-1919-1955*

I been in the mining company for 35 years underground. I worked for the Davidson, started out tramming and shoveling. I didn't live in the Davidson location, I boarded at first in the Piper House. Ed Curley run it. It's still there in Iron River, right across the street from IGA (Family Foods). They took care of the boarders pretty good. It was a nice life. Of course, I had a bed partner—he was on night shifts and I was on day shifts. Then in 1924, I come up here to Davidson Location.

Yah, when I first started underground, I went to the timekeeper and signed up, asking the captain for a job. Well, I had to lie about my age because I was too young. You had to be 21 to work in the mine and I was just a little over 17, I guess. Well, a year after when I come back again when they asked how old I was, I was 21 Again. I been that for three years when Bill Thomas says to me, "Jim, don't you ever get no older?"

Working at the mine, we'd fill up cars with shovels and push the cars out by hand. That was back about 1919. I was working here when the Davidson shut down in 1953 or 1954. P.M. bought out the Davidson so I worked for them, but the James had always been P & M—they were like the America Radiator Company, they changed every so often. But I worked for them. I worked for M. A. Hanna at the Hiawatha, and I worked for the Dober. And after I got laid off here at the Davidson, I went up to the Zimmerman mine in Gaastra and worked there for pretty near a year until that mine shut down. Then I went to the Carpenter in Crystal Falls. I worked there for maybe six months and we got shut down entirely.

When I first started, conditions were pretty tough. When you was blasting a chute, you'd get one car of dirt out and then you'd have to blast again, or else turn the air hose and blow the air out a little bit. You were working in smoke all day long. They didn't have no ventilation system. All the smoke went out through the drifts and up the shaft.

There were no compensation plans back then. Insurance, that's all. If you got hurt, you got your day's pay. How many days you were laid off, you got paid. This was the company's insurance plan. And then they had a company doctor, Dr. Irvine. He was the company doctor for years.

About contracting, the contracts always run by the foot. It was about two and a half dollars a foot for subdrifting and a dollar seventy-five for raising. Well, you'd have to put in two cuts a shift to make any money at all. You could only blast about five feet out of a cut maindrifting, because it was hard to break.

In the stopes, they got so much a car, and shoveling and maindrifting, they'd pay the maindrifters so much a foot—seven dollars a foot for maindrifting, but you had to make the drift eight by eight. But then all your work was by hand in the old days. We'd go in there and shovel out that drift and get it done as quick as we can and go home. That was our contract, to shovel the drift out and go home, three men.

When I started in 1919, that's the time we got our best pay in the mines. I was drawing $5.75 a day and after that it went down. The miners were getting $6.20 and we got $5.73. After that we got four dollars and some cents a day around 1930. You could go anyplace and get a job. I quit the James mine at dinner time. I got mad about something so I took my shower and changed my clothes and walked over to the Davidson and asked the captain for a job. He said, "Okay, come over in the morning."

My wife's brother-in-law couldn't get a job in 1917 or 18. They didn't talk English then. I know one mine I worked in had a big sign up over the door and the sign read, "If you're American by heart, talk American. If you can't talk it, learn it. And if you can't learn it, move."

I worked at the Davidson when they had mules here. When I first started, they were using carbide lights. From the first time I was down there, things changed a lot. We had our jumbos. They were a regular truck on the track. You had your two machines on the jumper so all you had to do for maindrifting was go in there, turn the crank and raise the machine up. Then drill your backholes and keep lowering. You had to stand there and turn the crank. As fast as the drill was going, you had to turn this crank just so it wouldn't hammer too much.

We used to put 24 holes in one cut, then we charged them and blasted them. It took one shift to drill a cut and then they had to shovel. Now they use "pneu" shovels. Well it didn't take no time to shovel a cut with them. You run back and hooked it up on the air, then you come back, give it the air, run it into the pile, turn another valve on the handle, and dump it over the top into the car. That beats shoveling by hand.

With a jumbo, we could put in a six foot cut a day main drifting. The hand way, you'd cut about four and a half feet, but the drifts would be narrower them days, just wide enough to get your motor and cars in. But when they got these big cars in, you had to widen your drift out for your air line and your water line and your discharge lines, and the tubing for the fans—all that had to go alongside the drift.

Politics? Well, the Davidson was a great Republican outfit. If they heard you were going to vote Democrat, they'd put in quite a kick. Maybe you'd get canned for it, if you were too strong of a Democrat. You had to keep your mouth shut.

My father worked in the mines way back in 1906,7,8—long before I can remember. I can just remember him coming home Saturday nights. He'd stay in town all week long and come home on Saturday nights. My mother took care of the farm—not much of a farm, just a few cows, a team of horses and a garden. He was a pumpman.

I remember a strike one time, but it only lasted a couple of days, but what they got out of it, I don't know. It was what you call a wildcat strike. They didn't want to eat underground. The mining company built us a nice big dining room down there, maybe 60 by 70 feet long and about 30 feet wide. And then they put nice tables in there and cement floors and wall. But they didn't want to eat underground, they wanted to come up to surface. So that time nobody went underground for a couple of days. But they settled it anyway and they went back.

They used to lay us off, the single men. They'd lay us off in the fall and hire us in the spring. Then in the fall, they'd lay us off again. They'd tell us they hated to do it, but to come back in the spring and they'd give you a job back. That was for stocking ore, they didn't want too big a stock pile. They did that the first few years I worked.

D.B. 6/1973

## JOHN JURECIC-*Tramming, Grievances and the Depression*

I came to this country in 1920 and it was hard times. We go down to Chatham—that is in Michigan, too. Cleveland Cliffs cut cordwood. So we went down there. They used it to make charcoal for the kiln and wood alcohol. I ended up working in the woods here for Harry Mertins who run that café. I needed to settle down, so I went in the Rogers mine. I see a place wet, pour it out. That time you shovel by hand when you blast. I put in one week, then I say, "No!" I quit. Then the guy coaxed me, "You gonna be all right. There's a good mine up there for the Verona, the Fogarty. So somehow, I went tramming.

The Unions started in the thirties when Social Security come. They tried to get a company representative, but, I say, what you gonna do with that? Some bosses was there (in the Independent union) and they're gonna tell you what to do. Then we start, I don't know which year, must be 1935 or 1937. We was a bunch with all the mines and we didn't know which one—AFL or CIO. We had a heck of a time. Our company was the first one. Happened I was the grievance man. Mr. Hanson was there yet, superintendent. Burkhamer come from Duluth, he was the district organizer. Me and another man and Frizzo and Ed Toni was there. He come in the office. He takes the contract, all right, and he went in the other room. Hanson and Stanley Brew was there. Then he come back. "You don't need no union," he say. "You bring the grievance to Mr. Hanson, and Hanson will fix you up with what you want." "No," Burkhamer say, "We want a union regardless. You don't want to sign, but the union is going to stay up here." He told him right out, and then we left. After we got enough men, the Labor Board say you got to have majority to call election. When we call the election, the company men wanted the independent union. We voted in the Fogarty dry, and we lost.

The CIO lost to the independent union. The independent union didn't do nothing for the men. They was all company men. We call them, excuse me, suckers, company suckers. They didn't do nothing so some of the men quit. It was only a dollar that time, union dues. Finally we start working and we got the majority. The second time we win. We was the first one in the county got the union, then the rest of them did.

To get in touch with the miners, we'd go from house to house, and talking in the mine. Then we called a meeting. When we started before, it was all the mines together. After, we had each company its own local. Bruno Hall, I remember was the first meeting. Then we had it in Caspian Hall most of the times. It was cheaper then, twelve dollars a year rent for the hall.

I had an accident in 1949. My drill hit a charge that didn't explode from the last shift. You can see it in my face. I lost a right eye. I had a family, five to raise. They want to put me on surface, but there was one guy, not blasted but a chip hit him—he lost 85% (vision). He was down in the mine yet. "No, no mining," they say, but I want to go. So I was put in. Another guy and I had seniority and more experience, so I filed a grievance. I got the job.

Then in 1960, it happened. All the miners was together. They didn't know if it was going to shut down or what. Me and John Lawnik was gonna go shift boss. And I didn't get it. Martini say, "What you want to do, run the motor, load the cars, go down the shaft and send the ore?" I could do anything. I said, "Listen, Martini, I don't have much more to go. I'm going to be 65 and the mine might shut down. How about scraping?" that was miner's pay, better pay than trammer boss. He said, "Good, but not mining". . . The fifteenth of March, the mine shut down.

**The Depression:** I remember Charlie Lawrence. That time when the mine was shut down, what do you call it, Hoover time. The company had a Model T, first truck. We worked three days a week. My last check was twenty-five dollars and some cents. He (Lawrence, Superintendent of the Verona Mining Co.) went on that truck and made a speech. He say, "Fella, it's going to be pretty tough time. You fellas, raise the chickens, get the cow, pigs, everything." He tell us. He say, "We got lots of land around." He gonna plow for us—he did, back of the mine in Caspian. We each got a piece to plant. And I bought a cow. I come home and tell my wife, "It's gonna be a tough time. That Lawrence, he know. I'm going to buy a cow." She say, "What you gonna do? Twenty-five dollars!" "Ya, I hear one guy from the James mine got a lot of cows." I go ask him. "Ya," he say, "pick any one, for twenty-five dollars. I'll even go with you." I buy one cow. In Caspian, they had a fence up, across the track there where they got the tower for the radio—and up in Berkshire, past Old Caspian on that hill, belonged to our company. They fenced that for us.

The company give us relief too. They said you got to pay it back, but we never paid back. Company come to the house every two weeks and give you the order. Trestrail would come there and the company nurse come and sometimes Hanson, too. Every woman would figure what she needs for the two weeks. They'd give her a slip and she'd go down to the store. They'd say, "You think what you need, but remember, you gonna pay back when you're working." You don't got the money, but got to eat. When they ask to pay back, I imagine the company did that instead of paying taxes.

D.B. 1/23/1974

## ANTON ROSETTI--*Tramming and Unionizing*

The miners in the stope had it dangerous, but tramming in a drift was just like being in a house. There was always danger, but iron mines aren't as bad as coal mines. There was danger when we worked down at the Homer. The stuff was too soft. We had to timber all over. I worked five years in the mine before I come to be a helper on the machine, the drill. They put you helper first. You can't go miner right away.

I was seventeen when I started work at the James mine as a trammer. You shoveled the cut. They blasted it out, then we had to clean it up with a wheelbarrow.

I worked at the Homer when I got miner's job, before I left for the army. Them days, there was lots of mines. It was no trouble to get a job. You don't like this mine, you got something to say, you get mad at a boss, you can go to the mining crews and ask for a job and they put you on right away. There was one young fella at the Homer got mad at a boss. He went up and changed his clothes—it was nine o'clock. He came over to the Davidson. The boss told him to get his clothes and go down right away. He only lost an hour or so. No trouble to get a job. But now the coming of Mr. Verona and M.A. Hanna, you got to watch out. If you walk out of one mine, you'll never get another one. That's right. Blackball.

. . . I run for Mine Inspector in the union. That's why they blackballed me, see? Before they don't know, but in the end, they said the gosh-jacked union was one of these what-cha-call-um? The guy who was the organizer of the union was like one of these that rules like Russia does. He was in the Communist Party. The organization was communist. But they couldn't prove anything because we didn't sign anything. They wanted us to sign communist just a few days before the election. But we wouldn't sign nothing.

Then we don't sign, that's why when the mine started up again, we lost out, we lost the election. That's why they called me an undesirable citizen. If we would have win, things would have been different. The government and the mine and everything would have been one big union if the union won the election, but we didn't make it.

He (my dad) told about the James, in the dry there was bunch Italian over there, bunch Cousin jack over here, Finlanders over there, Pollacks over there, and the superintendent didn't like that. Pretty soon he come down—I wasn't there, my dad told me. He (Dad) used to change up there with the bosses. He was a trammer boss. He used to change there with the captain, that's how he knows. The superintendent, he says, "I don't want to see this here very long. You fellas are wrong. Don't you know you're in the United States! You're not a Swede or an Englander. I want to see you fellas mixed up a little bit. Forget to talk your own nationality when you're on the job. Home you can do what you want. But on the job, you gotta talk United States so you know what's going on and you can take care of one another better. That was in 1899 or 1901. Now everything's mixed up and okay, but them days, oh boy, boy, boy!

I'm living today because of my neighbor. We was working on the seventh level…my neighbor was working fifty feet down. The cave come three times, first, then a little more, then he come big…We decided to go down to the next sub to get out of the wind. The other two were down and I was on the ladder going down when my neighbor shouted, "Let's go up, I found a nice place." Sure enough if we had gone down, after he comes the third time, water was coming down. The water was up on our waist belt. There was a rock twice as big as that refrigerator there. Everything was going down the shaft, fill up the shaft, too.

If we would have went down instead, we would have been one hundred feet under the water. That's the way it was with poor Minucchi. He died with two others. When he heard the wind coming at the start of a cave, he went over to a side drift. Water come with the cave and it filled up—trapped…He (Minucchi) tied himself up on the pipe with fuses he had in his pocket. He lived three or four days. It took that long to get up there to drill the cut. If we'd shoveled that out, we could have saved his life. The other two were dead with sand and gravel, laying down. This incident occurred in the Homer mine in 1930.

D.B.  1/16/1974

### VIVIAN FREDLUND--*Watchman, Hoistman, Dryman, Dumpster*

The first job I had with a mining company was when I was 15 years old. I worked during the summer vacation picking samples when the steam shovel ran. In those days, the sampler had to be young and agile—that is why I was hired, because every time the bucket dumped into an ore car, you had to jump down in the car and take a scoop. Now they sample the top of the car. You have a rope with nine knots on it about three feet apart and they put the rope on top of the pile and take a scoop-full from each knot. In those days we took a scoop full every time the buckets dumped. The Northwestern railroad cars weren't so bad. They had a board on the side about a foot wide so you had something to walk on. But then they came in with the Milwaukee Road cars. They only had a 2 X 4 on the edge that you had to walk on. When I wasn't sampling, I worked in the pit in front of the shovel. That was at the Davidson mine.

13

I had another job during summer vacation, too, at the Wapama-McGreevy mine adjoining the Forbes mine. I was just a youngster and they wanted someone for a watchman because the mine was closed. They had a man who was disabled in the mine watchman at night for 12 hours, from six to six. I was watching from six to six in the daytime and the pay wasn't very much – 50 cents a day. I found out from this other fellow he was getting a dollar and a half, so I quit. I worked from 1929 to 1942 for the Copper Range Company. Then, we moved down here to the Forbes Location. I worked then for four years for the Davidson. I was a lander. In the winter time he operates the transfer of the ore to the stockpile and in the summer he loaded the railroad cars.

Then in 1946 they had a big layoff . . . They laid off about fifty men and I was about seventh from the bottom in seniority so I got laid off. I wasn't out of work very long. I got a chance to go over to the Sherwood mine and they called that work landing, too, but there the lander was a dumpster operator. A dumpster is a Koehning vehicle that has a box in front and the operator sits behind you—you can see them there on the Sherwood stockpile. One shift and I would be on the dumpster and the next I'd operate the crusher. Then I got put as a relief man on the hoist. Hoistman is a desirable job. It requires skill but it's clean work and better than other surface work. For the last five years I was at the Sherwood I operated the hoist.

The company houses were shelter, but they didn't have modern conveniences. We didn't have indoor plumbing and for a while we didn't even have water—we had to go to a central place to get a pail of water and bring it into the house. That meant Saturday night bath in a washtub. It started out with the officials getting these modern conveniences and later everybody got them.

In recent years, the mining companies disposed of these houses. They sold them to the tenants. The one I have, I bought from the company. I never thought I would own a house. When the people bought the houses, they took interest in them and improved them a lot. They all fixed up with roofing and siding and we all have bathrooms and garages.

D.B. 7/1973

## OLIVER WESTER--*Shift Boss and Lander*

I worked two months before I was drafted for World War II. I was with the M.A. Hanna Company at the Hiawatha #2, which formerly was the Dober Mine. I was discharged from the service in October, 1945 and went back into the mine immediately. I was given the job of landing on the surface. I ran the trolley out from the shaft as the skips came up and unloaded and I hauled them out to the stockpile of ore.

The superintendent at the mine approached me one day saying or asking me if I would be satisfied to stay there or if I would want to go into the engineering department. I said that I would try it. He told me to report to the main office on Monday morning to George Kohler in the engineering department and that's when I started in the department and eventually Mr. Quayle, who was the general manager at the time, called me in and asked me if I wanted to go out to the Homer Mine as a foreman, which I did.

I was foreman underground (shift boss in other words). I had shift work—alternating days, afternoons and nights. I visited each gang which consisted of two men in the process of drifting, maindrifting, subdrifting, raising and things pertaining to the mining.

Drifting is you have a base and you want to make a maindrift normally roughly 8 x 8 . They (miners) drilled holes with a jumbo and charged and blasted and cleaned up the dirt in advance that way every 8 feet. There were 18 levels in the Hiawatha #2. That was a deep mine—over 2000 feet deep. Temperature varied but not very much. It was normally around 45 degrees steady.

The first thing you do when you hit the ore body is you put in a the main drift. After you put in the main drift, you put in a scraper drift at that time or chute (it varied in the area) and you drove the scraper drift in roughly 8 feet above the floor of the main drift in that area and that usually ranged in size from 6' x 8' or so and then there were raises which were off of the scraper drifts up into the area that normally was

14

between 30 to 40 feet up. Then there were subdrifts up and then there was the mining raise on the end of this scraper drift that went up and they started stoping—by stoping I mean slicing, breaking and blasting the dirt down—and it would end up in the scraper drift and then you used the tugger to scrape the dirt out onto the main drift which was rails and cars and motors there to transport that out to the shaft.

You were mining up all the time. Each sub. Usually the subdrifts were 200 foot intervals between the two main drifts. In other words, there was a ladder road put up all the way up to 200 feet and that ladder road or the raise was about 4 feet in diameter that held the ladder road. Then off of the ladder road, then 30 to 40 foot subs , they drifted in with a subdrift which was maybe 4 x 6 or 4 x 8 in that area into a raise that was put up on the end of the scraper drift at thirty foot levels up to the main drift above and then they started stoping around this mining raise at the end and then work back. They mined so much around the mining raise on the first sub and then moved up to the second sub and kept working that way and then working back. There were pillars in between and these were a safety device…one time, I had to go through this ladder road and I stepped off the ladder and the station went and I fell down. I ended up on the sub below. I had fallen about twenty some feet or so.

My job in the engineering department was to mark out the route of the drifts and also put lines in the main drifts and the subdrifts. The iron ore in the scraper drift—they scraped it out and then there was a grizzly like over the back of the main drift and there were cars underneath that they scraped the ore into. The grizzly is a structure made of rail like a chute with a hole in it so that the dirt would fall in this area right over the track into the cars. A motorman moved the cars. When he was all loaded up, he takes the ore to the shaft and they have a pocket there that when the dirt is dumped into the pocket, the skip tender in turn then loads the skip at the bottom of the pocket into skips and rings the bell and sends the skips up. The cars were side dumping.

A crusher was located in the main shaft right below the pocket. Dust in the mines was taken care of with fans. In early days, you used to hear about black lung, but the air circulation was better in later years when I was working. Hearing was a problem especially these miners using jackhammers drilling. They should have been wearing earplugs and of course safety glasses—that's the rule.

When somebody is injured, there's usually men working somewhere in the area and they'll get a hold of the foreman right away and then we'd go and do exactly what we had to do in removing the injured. There's a basket and everything there close to the shaft so it was available in the event you had to use it. The worst accident I saw was a cave-in and the man didn't make it.

There were mining inspectors to check safety features and inspect maps. I remember Bull Melchiori and one from Crystal Falls, Reino Anderson. Bull was a miner before becoming a mining inspector—I'm not sure about Reino.

I ended up at the Groveland the last 10 years I worked. First when I got down there, I was in the pellet plant—that's where we made the material that went through the furnace—baked it or fired it—and hauled it out on the conveyor belt out to the stockpile. It was a 24 hour operation, seven days a week. You didn't have a choice—you were assigned hour shift and you had your crew. I'd say there were at least 12 in it. I slipped and broke my leg in the plant and then I worked up in the engineering department for a while until I could get along and then I went into the pit as a pit foreman. That was outside and in the winter, it was freezing cold. I used to be in those trucks going up and down the ramps and it was really something.

H.B. 5/18/2001

**JESS KOSKY--*Underground Miner and Blaster***

I started working in the mine after I got out of the service in World War II. I started with Hanna Mining Company on May 24, 1946. I spent twenty-five years underground at the Wauseca.

First of all, I was a day laborer. I shoveled here and you're shoveling there—you're a helper. You were just another man. After you had a period of time underground then they put you with an experienced miner—and you learned to develop.

You know you have main drifts going that the cars and motors travel. Then there are scraper drifts that went crossways over the main drifts. And they have chutes. And they have up there tuggers and scrapers, and it's a drift about 7 x 9 feet and then you got raises going out up into the ore body and you develop and drive these raises up. You had to have them 4 x 4. You have a machine that's called a Murphy Machine and it's the God-awfullest machine you've ever seen. There's no way to pick it up and carry it that you're comfortable with it. You can't put it on your shoulder, it's out of balance. We used to call it Mother Murphy. And you run these raises up and in one end you run the raise up and it's what you call a lateral and in the back the opposite side of the scraping drift, you run a raise all the way up to the ore body which was 300 feet up to the next level. You climbed every morning. You had to have a powder bag of 50 pounds. You had to have maybe 15 fuses and you needed planking or rods. So when you were climbing up that thing 300 feet, man it kept you in shape and you could not go without something all the times. In your place of work, you had to have three sets of rods cause if they break you couldn't go down and get some more. Everything was in coordination that you had to know what you were doing.

When you climb the ladder, both hands are free and you've got everything on your back or shoulder. We used to make ropes and then if we had rods, we would tie them on the ropes on one shoulder and had the powder bag on your back. And every 44 feet there was a sub-level and you would drift from the lateral to what they called a breaking raise where the ore body is. This lateral raise is in rock because you've got to leave that in there so that if you had to get back in there for any reason the lateral will stay there and doesn't cave in. And every 44 feet you run a drift—they call it a subdrift and it goes right down in this raise that I'm talking about the breaking raise on the end. And that's the way you stop and you pull back and they're usually 90 feet wide, the stopes and you've got a pillar of 40 feet.

The stope is 300 feet between levels and the last subdrift is maybe 35 feet from the level, so you could be up on top 270 feet looking down. But you don't see it. Like I said that black is a saving thing. If you had lights where you could see everything, you'd probably have to get out of there like the rats did. You know years ago, they had the canaries where if the canary died, get out because there was bad air.

Dynamite is a funny thing—it had to be fresh. You do not fool with dynamite. You get it 45, you get it 70 and you get it 95 strength. The glycerin in it if it set in one place for a long time falls to the bottom— that's when there's danger. You tap it in so that the sticks are safe. What you do with the stick is you slice it with a knife a little bit so it packs in. Otherwise it would drop out. We usually used 40 to 45 strength dynamite. First of all there was 8 inch by 1 ˜ inch. Then we got the 17 x 2 inch. We used to call them balonies. It was much easier charging with them, but you had to drill a bigger hole if you had a 2 incher.

We used ammonium nitrate. We called it sheep manure. I was one of the first ones to use it—Milton Saxon and I. When it came to the Wauseca everybody was against it, but we were told we had to use it. It was much cheaper and if it was used right, it did the same job because we used it in the stopes. When we had that month of testing it, we got called everything but a man! It wasn't our fault, we just couldn't say no to the bosses. So, it did just as good a job as dynamite does.

It came in a fifty pound bag and we had a gun and we had an inch and a quarter hose and you put it in and you start from the end of the hole and just as soon as you see some prills coming back, you pull it back—you pull it back and you learned in no time how to fill the hole. You filled it and then when you got within 5 feet from the end, you pulled out and you put the detonator in. When you set the detonator in you put in another two feet of ammonium nitrate.

Some people had the blast at lunchtime. As far as the stopes were concerned, they blasted at quitting time because they had a big area. When you were developing, you couldn't make nothing on one cut a day. And if you had to have one place to work, you had to have two cuts so you had to have your cut 4 by 6 feet. The most you could make in a day was three. We were paid by the foot. Every place was different.

You had to understand what you were building and how many holes you had to put in. You didn't put in the same number of holes every place that you went. The first day you drill a center hole and that'll

16

determine what kind of ground you have. Then you drilled it within two inches on each side, another hole the same length. We called that burning out the center. Then you put in cutting lines. They start on maybe from the center a foot or more and they go at an angle so your six inches from where the other holes ended up. Then you've got the center of it out. When you get the center out then the rest is nothing but slicing it back down. But say if I got good ground, I put a six foot cut in and I probably put in ten holes. If I got six foot ground, then I can drill a six foot cut and put in ten holes. But if I go back and I see that I've lost a foot of that ground, I cut it back to either a four foot or look and see where I lose the distance of the cut. If it's in the center, I cut another hole and try it again, it's a little experimentation when you're going underground. It depends on the texture and the hardness, too. That's the main thing underground—knowing exactly what you can do with it.

I was safety man for ten years before I went to the Groveland. On a specified day I would go with the shift boss and captain and say there were two or three safety men, we'd go through every place and we'd discuss the working procedure there. We had to make sure that changes were made to keep the company and the men safe. You looked at the ground and you checked the possible hazards and you put that on a list and ran it through with the superintendent. The men had to change and the company would have to change sometimes unless it would cost them a lot of money, you know. The safety man was an important job underground.

H.B.  5/17/2001

## DAVID A. RAIHA--*Slicer*

I was born in Stambaugh, MI in 1914. We lived in Stambaugh for possibly four years, then we moved to what they call the Dober Location because my father worked for the Oliver Mining Company and those were Oliver Mining Company homes so he got to rent one there.

It was just a frame home and there weren't too many rooms. The first house we went into was a small one-story home. That was next door to the one we actually ended up with—a story and one-half home. There was a mixture of people in that area—Italian, Finnish, and Croatian also. We lived there until we moved out to the Anderson Pit Road in Stambaugh side of Iron River and then eventually they sunk a new shaft on the other side where Raymond Iron Works is now. That's where the Oliver Mining Company sank a new shaft and he (father) worked there too. He worked until the depression—about 1932 or 1933. They were still working three days when they finally closed it down for the depression. Once it (the mine) closed down, he never went back. He was examined but Dr. Libby was company doctor and he didn't let him go back into the mine because of high blood pressure.

I remember they used mules underground and they used to bring them to the surface for a rest every once in a while. Then they would take them back down.

During the depression we had plenty to do on the forty acres because it was all hand work, you know. When the WPA came along, I worked on a road with the team for a while. My father got work when the WPA came along too, but it couldn't be more than $44.00 a month. Whenever they did work that called for horses, they kind of took a team from here or two teams or whatever and we got $7.50 a day for a team and a driver. Sounds good, huh?

We had food and milk but no money. I can always remember that silver dollar was in the cupboard on one shelf and nobody ever touched it, but there came a time during the depression when flour was $2.00 for that hundred pound sack and they had to use that silver dollar because there wasn't any money. You couldn't buy flour from no one because who's gonna trust you when nobody's working?

I went into the mines in 1937. It was the Bengal Mine where I worked and they opened that mine up and they were hiring young men like myself who didn't know anything about mining. They had all the older guys already there that went back to work as soon as they got a chance and then they hired younger to carry on when the older ones couldn't work anymore. The older ones were forty years old or maybe a little older.

My first job at the mine was called slicing. It was producing iron ore. They had what they called a raise. That came from the main level—it was actually just a hole. They started from the main level and up and they went as high as they had to go to be in the ore body. Then these contracts they called them—each two miners had a contract. It was just called a contract because it was a place where you worked. You started from this raise because that's where the iron ore was scraped into and it went down and then they loaded it on tram cars at the bottom. There wasn't too many slice mines around. It was slicing because it was soft—it wasn't the real hard iron ore at all. That's how I started. It had to be timbered as you blasted six feet out. You had the timber right up to what they call the breast and then you drilled and blasted again, scraped that out with an electric scraper they had, and then you put another set of timbers which were maple or birch or even tamarack, and then you put poles across what they call cedar lagging. It was split cedar and –that's how I was working at first.

As far as safety is concerned, because you went in with this slice, you also laid hardwood boards, some lumbering outfit was selling the boards, so you laid boards in there. They were various lengths and had to be over six feet long to span that. When you took out six feet you covered it with these boards. Consequently when you mined out up here and then you went underneath there, all that lumber was on top of your head yet, so you had to brace it up there with those timber sets. Otherwise underneath that tremendous weight they would have come down. I don't think there were any fatalities on my shift, None. We had no qualms about working there. The Bengal Mine was never a stope mine.

The Bengal Mine was wet. There was two or three owners—Swanson and there was Young. The Young side was dry and the Swanson side was wet. I mean you wore rain gear all the time…It was the same mine as the Cannon, except the Cannon sank a new shaft there. When I went to work at the Bengal there was a shaft there already. The shafts were hoisting the ore and there was also a shaft where the men went down. They had to sink a third shaft and they called it the ventilation shaft.

We didn't have to pay for our dynamite, but we had to pay for pipe wrenches because they had a habit of disappearing. We had to always tighten the joints—everything was run by air down underground— we also had to tighten the couplings. There was a water pipe and an airline, which went into each working place so we had to have pipe wrenches, but they were just the right size.

The unions were in 1938,1939 and 1940—the United Steelworkers. I believe I still have my Union Card.

I worked until 1944 and then left for good.

H.B.  6/13/2001

## DAVID TARSI--*Danger and Black Rock*

I started at the Beta Mine at Dead End in 1907. Then I work for Homer. Now they call it different names. Them days, they call it Wickwire. Now they call him M.A. Hanna. Then I work for J and L (Jones and Laughlin Mining Co.). Then the Davidson. Then Konwinski, now they call it Wauseca—see, they always change the names and the company, I suppose. James Mines, Spies Mine, Virgil Mine, McGreely— that's all the mines (I work in) on this side. Maybe I work one year or a couple of years. But when I get mad I never report. I won't out my partner. I was good myself.

Some mines was open pit. You go back and you never see nothing. There was danger. Homer Mine, you never see one month you didn't have two or three dead bodies. Danger. And I was there myself, that's the worst. If you don't watch yourself, nobody else will.

I worked there in the Virgil Mine in 1914. There was big open. The Wickwire was around that mine. And since I was there one fella got killed on the skip. "Cause in them days, we no had elevator (cage) to come up in. We had to ride on the skip, no roof. Six at a time, we ride that skip. To ring the bell for going up or down, we had a wire, any kind of wire, from the shaft to the crew, from the surface engine house where we got the engine to pull you up and down. But no juice. So it happened that day, it was that fellow up there, Jesus Christ, must of tell me not to go to work. I stayed home. Do you believe in anything like that? And the fella got killed coming up in that cage. There were four, one on each corner, and two on top calling bell. And the cable, that wire that they ring for going up and down, broke off. On the way going up, the wire got caught around his neck. It pulled him off, and he went down to the bottom of the shaft, crushed all to pieces pretty near. You bet, that's the danger we had them days.

You want to find out about the black rock? You know the black rock, when it get loose, it get hot. In powder it catch fire. It's the sulphur in the black rock. One time that happened at the Davidson. He had a big open full of that loose black rock. This black rock came on fire and he burn. But he was in luck because the smoke only could go up and it couldn't hurt anybody in the mine. But some way he had to get him down. He know that black rock makes room up there full of fire. You drill all this back and break it down, for the reason, I don't know…The shift boss was with them. There was three guys, two miners and a shift boss. So dumb, stupid that's what I call them! The blast went off. Voorrum! Fire and smoke shoot right through to them guys, kill them right there like you sit on that chair. You never move. He had a door (bulkhead) but it never close a thing. That's why he wanted everybody out of the mine. But they stay there to see what the fire done. Yeah! Smoke come down and shoot fire and cook all three right there. They never moved one step. You see what black rock mean? Black rock is a bugger. Then you use a drill with a machine and that black rock can make dust. You get out of there.

The dust stick on your lung. Then, like I know, you spit him out, they come out of you. I'm full of black rock myself. I went to Ironwood to sue the company, but I didn't have enough…then the doctor sent a note. Dave Tarsi not allowed to work on the black rock because he got quite a bit in him. So, I worked for five days and then they took me out. Cap said, "I gotta take you out of here." Nice, nice fella. "Well," I said, "I'm no good here, I'm no good there, I'm not good nowhere." He said, "You're a good man, Tarsi. We can put you anywhere, anyplace, any system, you can do it. But for your own good on account of the black rock in your lungs, you ain't allowed to work in it. " Thank you, thank you very much! I was glad. I ended up working on the stope on iron ore. That's where I made the best (wages) in my life.

D.B.  6/15/1972


## EARL KNIIVILA--*Ore Grader*


I graduated from high school in 1932 which was the height of the great depression and work was scarce and I didn't start working anywhere really until the WPA and ERA Programs went into affect and I worked there until 1936. I started working for the Forestry Service in  Iron River in 1936 and April 1, 1937 I started to work for Hanna. I went into the Ore Grading Department. Albin Olson from Gaastra was the ore grader and he needed help and I was hired to help him. I worked there until he retired and then I was shifted out to the Hiawatha Mine as a timekeeper for a couple of years. After that I came back.

What I did later on was took care of the general recording of the data which we needed in the department, data from the lab (sample analyses). We took the car numbers down over the phone from the mines, the car numbers of the cars that were loaded the previous twenty-four hours. I did a lot of the paperwork for Albin Olson. He was getting close to retirement age and he needed help. Shortly after that, he had a breakdown and had to leave.

The ore was analyzed for iron, phosphorous, manganese, silica, aluminum, and moisture. The ore contents varied from mine to mine quite a bit and from day to day. The higher manganese ore was found in the Cannon, the Bengal and some in the Rogers, but the Hiawathas and the Homer and a grade at the Cannon were lower manganese. The ore in this area is primarily a higher "phos" ore—anywhere from .3 to .6 percent phosphorous.

To explain the Bessemer grade of ore, it is a low "phos" ore—the lowest. The maximum "phos" allowed in a Bessemer grade ore is .045 percent phosphorous. Anything above that up to about a .2 or .250 is considered a low "phos" ore—anything above is considered a high "phos" ore.

The Wauseca had a fairly high phosphorous ore. It would go up to .5 percent. The Hiawathas probably average a .4 and the Homer anywhere from .3 up to .450. In our company, National Steel, the blast furnaces wanted nothing above .4. So we had to grade to that.

At the blast furnaces they used a mixture of ore from many sources. The Mesaba Range in Minnesota was considerably lower in 'phos". The ores from the Iron River area were mixed with the lower "phos" ores and the charge was put into the furnace. When the blast furnace was charged, they used the same recipe to arrive at a certain blend to arrive at a certain chemical analysis of the pig iron. That never changed…it was always the same.

When ore was loaded, a sample came out of every car—and many places in that car. The sampler had a rope with knots in it and he would put that rope over the car lengthwise in three different places—close to the edge, in the center (and on the other edge) and he would take his sample from wherever that knot was. There was a scoop that would take a half a cup full—if you can imagine an eight-ounce cup, it would take about half of that. He would sample the cars and put that into the car and it was brought to the central lab at the Homer.

When ore was brought up from underground, it was put into cars we called direct shipping. We sampled in a five-car sample to make up one…and that was numbered and designated as to grade. When that sample arrived at the lab, it was crushed fairly fine and then a sample was taken of that sample. Only a small amount of ore was needed to analyze it. (An ore train was always divisible by five) But, in direct shipping ore and stockpile loading, the ore was more uniform so a sample was taken of ten cars. So we could identify the ore in the cars by the mine, the mine grades and the sample number. That's how the docks would identify the ore that they wanted to use. (A train) could be a mixture of the Hiawathas, Homer-Wauseca and it could be Buck ore from the Pickands-Mather mine.

Normally there would be two or three trains a day. In the old days when they used steam locomotives there were about fifty or sixty cars. When the diesels came into being, why they went up to 100. They sometimes had three or even four diesels (on a train). The railroad was experimenting to see how many engines (locomotives) they would need to haul, but unfortunately the drawbars on the car weren't strong enough so when they got above 100 cars, the drawbars would come apart and the train would stall. Each car held 70 tons. Sometimes they would really load the cars up and they'd be about 75 tons, which was too heavy.

There was a period of time when the standard locomotive wasn't powerful enough to pull a train especially up the grade out of the Stambaugh Yards up to Caspian so they would take a pusher in at the end of the train to help push the load and the train up the grade and then it would drop off. Later on the engines got more powerful. When they switched to diesels, the diesels had no problem.

I went into the service in 1944. I put my two years in and was discharged in 1946. I came back to Hanna and went to work immediately as a timekeeper for a period of time. After about a year, I went into ore grading and did that most of the rest of the time I worked here. There was also a period when I kind of floated around. Remember when the Bates Mine closed because of caving underground? At the time they just closed the door and left everything as it was—all the warehouse supplies were still there—everything was left underground and eventually all that equipment had to be accounted for. The company had to write it off somehow, so I was out there taking inventory in the warehouse and doing some accounting for the main office downtown so they accounted for all the stuff to write off.

When the mines closed here a lot of the miners were transferred to the Groveland or else they took their retirement. I couldn't see the 45 mile trip to the Groveland every morning, so I took the Hibbing transfer. It was the same kind of work. Up there it (ore left) was a lower grade material that had to go through a concentrating plant similar to what goes on in the pellet plant prior to the pelletizing. They had to use a process to eliminate the material that wasn't wanted to raise the grade up to what we called merchantable ore.

(To return here) As I understand it, there was ore left underground when the mines closed simply because it wasn't economical to mine it and hoist it out and ship it. It's a matter of costs. As long as the pellet plants are operating, these mines will not open as far as I can see. If pellet plants run out of crude ore, I would guess that there is so much foreign ore available that can be mined fairly economically too that they would have to mine all that out and get rid of it before they'd ever come back here. This ore is so deep and I can't imagine that they'd ever go down that deep in an open pit process. The Hiawatha would have a pit a mile wide. They can't pelletize our ore because it's not a magnetic type.

H.B.  5/8/2001

## ROBERT "ACE" BODEN-*Stemmer*

When I got out of High School, I went into the service and when I got out of the service in May of 1945, I got a job in the mine and I've been here ever since. I started in the Homer Mine as a stemmer. When anyone in the mine needed a partner, they would send a stemmer with them. So, I started out doing all various jobs in the mine…As a stemmer, it was normally one or two days. Sometimes it was longer if the guy was really sick, but 99 chances out of a hundred it was either one or two days.

I was surprised that I really enjoyed working underground. It was the same temperature all the time. You got a little wet, but outside of that you never froze off anything and the only thing actually you had to worry about were safety precautions and lack of air. I think that's the reason that the majority of the miners smoked. Due to the fact that they lit a match and if it went out, get out of there! Or if you were puffing on a cigarette and you couldn't puff anymore, it was dead so you got out of there in a hurry.

I was a Stemmer, but I ended up taking some ICS Courses and ended up on the hoist—underground hoist and I stayed there until the mine shut down.  Actually there were two hoists in the Homer Mine. One was the main hoist that they went down from surface and then they walked in there on the seventh level and there was a sub hoist that went down to the tenth level. When the men went, they spread all over and they would take the hoist on the seventh level going down to the eighth, ninth, and tenth level and, of course, that would leave the big hoist to be used for taking up the ore.

Actually, we never did hoist much ore on the small hoist. It was mostly men and supplies. But the big hoist they had a lot of poundage. The big hoist took up men, but when it took up ore it had a separate cage—what they call a skip—for the ore.

There was water in the mine, but it wasn't drastic. When I first started, I used to go over to the Cardiff quite a bit and check the pumps. They had seventeen surface pumps. We used to have a good time down there in the mine. We had one old fellow, the pump man, and he was always laying down and he had his hand out like this and if the water came up it would wake him up. If the pump went out, he'd made sure that it was started again. We used to take his pipe out of his mouth when he was sleeping and we'd scrape it out and we'd put snuff in it and then we'd put the pipe back there and ring the alarm. He'd get up and look all around at what's going on, then he'd start lighting that pipe with snuff.

You got to know everyone. There was monkeying around right from when you start dressing to go underground to when you got out of the shower and were dressing.

One time a Vidas had a Model T and came to work at the Homer and the guys used to lift it up and put blocks underneath it because he had started it by the wheels. They put blocks under all four wheels and he got in it and started it and was trying to go and trying to go.

Cooney was working on surface and he took Koski's pick-up and he opened up the windows and put timber through the doors. This guy was hauling gravel so he gets the truck all full of gravel. He found out that Cooney did it and took a load of gravel to his house across from the mine and dumped the whole load on the front steps. He told his wife that Cooney wanted a load of gravel and he wanted it dumped right there! There was a lot of crazy things.

I had a total of thirty-three years in completely. I think I had the last ten years at the Groveland. At the Groveland (in Dickinson County), we had to start all over again. They never had such a thing as stemmers because everything was on top. It was just common labor—you went and you waited for your chance if a job was up and you went and took the test for it. If you got the job, then you went there.

H.B.  4/23/2001

### GEORGE KOEHLER--*Superintendent of the Cannon Mine*

We had trouble getting the shaft down to the ledge. We finally made it and sunk the shaft down to 1,635 feet. That is certainly not a deep mine in comparison with others.

(Mining is a matter of economics). It depends on the quantity of ore you have. That's what the whole thing is about. . . Is the ore worth that much and can you sell it? Is there enough iron content, is the sulphur and phosphorous in the ore of percentage that you can sell it to the blast furnaces. Since I've been here there were thirteen to fifteen iron mines in this area, known as a high phosphorous area. Along about 1958 or 1959, we started to see pellet plants, an open pit proposition whereby you can mine your ore from the surface. We call them agriculturalists, not miners. You mine it from the surface and this type of ore is practically phosphorous and sulphur free and the iron content is down to thirty-three to thirty-five percent. It takes about three tons of this surface material to make one ton of pellets. But when you get the pellets, you have a concentration of this ore which brings the iron percentage up to sixty or sixty-five percent in a lot of cases, without the sulphur and phosphorous and very low silica…The blast furnace men, the steelmakers like it.

That accounts for the competition. That was a big reason. We could see the handwriting on the wall a long time ago, 1958. When any of these steel companies can buy pellets, even at a premium price, they don't want natural ore.

Economics. We had closed the Cannon Mine already. The Hiawatha Mine with the two shafts were two of the best producers in this district. The grade of ore was probably the best there was here. We operated the Hiawatha No. 1 until it was practically exhausted. The Hiawatha No. 2 lasted a little bit longer, then that was shut down. All that was left was a hole in the ground, although, we had done a lot of back filling in the stopes, the voids where the ore was mined out. That enabled us to take the pillars, but you had to be careful.

What was left were the Homer mine and the Wauseca. The product from those mines was hardly acceptable to the blast furnaces. They were high in sulphur and phosphorous.

D.B.  8/10/1973

# LIFE IN A MINING COMMUNITY

### R. C. RETALLACK, M. D.--*Practicing Medicine in a Mining Town*

I arrived here April 1, 1940. When I first arrived, the mining companies had a hospital in Stambaugh called the Stambaugh General Hospital. It was owned by the mining companies primarily for their own injuries, to take care of mining accidents.

22

However, we doctors were allowed to use it at will for surgery and sick patients. Many of them, of course, were miners or miners' families, as a major part of the population at that time were working for the mines. The mining company had good insurance, and the hospital practically paid for itself—although sometimes it was in the red. The mining company didn't bother with that—they could write it off. Since the mining companies have moved out, the people of the area have voted a millage to build a new hospital. The old hospital has been turned over to the city. It's still vacant, but to meet the requirements of the State Health Department, it was too expensive to remodel the old hospital.

When I first came here, I worked for a salary with Dr. Irvine. My practice here was interrupted in 1942 when I enlisted in the service. I served as an Army surgeon and general surgeon in the South Pacific. That gave me a lot more experience. When I came back, I stayed with Dr. Irvine for a year or two, then I built my own office here.

Dr. Irvine was a company doctor. The company doctor, in this area anyway, was paid a certain fee each month for every man on the payroll. Dr. Irvine received that fee. That was the arrangement with the company. However, what surgery he did on any of the patients, their insurance covered that. Pickands Mather and Inland Steel had their own choice of company doctors. Mostly they had Dr. Cooper and he has since deceased. Now they go to any of us doctors. I think Dr. Nora does most of the yearly examinations. The company doctors that I know of always had very good rapport with the patients. Of course, they (the patients) had freedom of choice, too. But if they went some place else, they had to pay for their office calls. When I first came up here, the company doctor always furnished simple medicines like cough syrup and aspirins and that sort of thing, but nothing that required expensive medication.

D.B.  1/15/1975

## THE MINING LOCATION--*Photograph and memories*

In early days few miners owned transportation means to take them to work and back. Mining companies built so called "locations" in the vicinity of their mines and rented the homes constructed there to the miners for a dollar a room. Miners could then walk to their work.

Recreation centers such as one finds at the Baltic and Old Caspian areas were also built. Classes were given in English to assist miners and their families in passing the tests for citizenship. Showers, which were not part of the individual homes, were installed for men to use. One night a week was reserved for the women. Evening activities were also scheduled such as dancing and card playing.

## ANNA PISONI--*Boarding Housekeeper*

My story is long, is big. I was born in Norway, Michigan, and then my mother she sent me to Sporminore, Austria, when I was three years old and I was living with my aunties over there…My father came over to see me and he was preparing to bring me back to America again—I was thirteen year old then. Then he changed his mind...I was about eighteen year old when they took me back with them to Stambaugh.

My poor father don't have no luck. He was working for the Baltic mine and he lost his life. That was exactly how many years? It was May 28, 1904 when he lost his life. He had a job to dumping the ore into the car…But this day he (Billy Jobe, Supt) said, "Listen, I'm going to help you out for a while"…My father said to Billy Jobe, "I give you strictly order, just leave one car go down alone"—the empty cars was coming from the shaft that way to my poor father at the pocket, because he said, "If you got one car if the brake is no good, it will be all right alone." Billy Jobe, go up and leave that car to come down to fill it. Any you know him, he let two cars come down at the same time, not one, but two. My father was standing on the car beneath the pocket. The shock of hitting was so much that my poor father lost his control and fell down in the track and he lost his life right there. He was only 48.

Billy Jobe came to the house crying. "It's my fault. I'm to blame. You won't go hungry. Your family will be well take care of." Yah, three months later he kick her (mother) out of the company house. Those days were bad. There was no social security, there was no compensation and my poor mother was getting a little help from the county, but it's a good thing that we always had boarders. We was working hard making a go of it as best we could.

We made a living keeping boarders, seven boarders in our home, not a big place. I was there until I was about 19 year old and then I got married. My mother built a big rooming house, three stories in Palatka. She built it after father got killed—she got money from the company. In 1906 she built it. They call in Calliari's Hotel; my mother's name is Maria Calliari. She had opera house and bakery shop with her hotel.

To run a boarding house, I tell you, it was a hard life. You got to get up early in the morning, work hard many hours. We had the space down here (Virgil) for 34 boarders. We had that pretty near full sometime. Some come, some go. But it was not bad. We make our living pretty good.

The trouble was, it was not as convenient in those days. We had to get our water outside, pump it from the well, wash by hand on these old little washer boards. It was all hard labor.

People came from everywhere. We had quite a few English fellas, and then we have some Swede and some Finn, the most was Finnish people. Oh, it was a mixture, but they go along pretty good. Once in a while you find some was a little hot headed. And we have to get up early in the morning—4:00, because they was working then 10 hours a day. They left at six and came back after five. They take their dinner pail and come back evenings past five.

We had a heavy breakfast in the morning, potatoes, pancakes, eggs and bacon. We had to feed them heavy because they were working hard. They wanted more than toast and coffee. We had two or three cows for milk and then I had maybe one hundred chicken and we killed maybe two or three pigs in the fall. Sometimes we would buy a calf and butcher it ourselves. It was too expensive to buy everything from the store. We always had a garden. We raised our own potatoes.

They had those round tin pails in those days and they were stacked. In the bottom you put the coffee and above that came a good sandwich with meat, a double sandwich maybe with boiled egg, Then a piece of pie or cookies or cake. Those guys worked hard and was very hungry. They like to eat.

Monday was the washing day. We washed the miner's street clothes and the linen, but not the mining clothes. They took care of (them) themselves. They took it down town to the Chinese laundry or on Saturdays they'd go to the dry house to wash mining clothes. Women in town did laundry, but never mining clothes. Was like red grease.

Breakfast took a while. If we had to make pancakes, we had to get up earlier than 4 o'clock to heat the griddle. It took a while. That was more work. At breakfast they were all there. We had 35 boarders for breakfast. There was a place for twelve men at each table. After breakfast we had the dishes to wash and clean up, make the beds upstairs. I pack lunch pails early in the evening because it took a long time to pack those pails. I just put in the coffee or tea in the morning. I went to bed at ten o'clock or before.

D.B. 5/1973

## ETHEL HOCKING--*Housewife*

I came to Iron River March 16, 1916 from the Isle of Man. At the time I came they were shipping a lot of ore because there were lots of active mines around.

I lived in Caspian when I was married. I could walk over to the mine and take my husband's lunch to him. We could do that before the union came in and made rules. The safety people came at the same time and stopped people. They put fences around to stop anybody from coming in. I used to love to go to the engine room and watch my husband work. I would take a pasty to him for his supper and take my knitting and stay for the rest of the evening.

He didn't go down in the mine very much. He did work a little while helping the plumbers with the water lines to pipe the drinking water down. He worked in the boiler room first and learned how to operate the boilers and provide the steam for the engines—they were all run by steam at that time. Then he graduated up to be a brakeman as they called it, or a hoisting engineer is the proper word. He worked both on the ore and the man hoist. The men at the mine used to tell me that he was a very good man on the hoist because he give a steady quick ride and he never bumped on the bottom. So it was fun watching him. I like to see how he was working. He explained how the machinery worked to me. I became an engineer myself. At least I used to say I could run the boilers myself if the shovel were small enough. He used a great big scoop shovel for the coal.

We lived in the Caspian location. We had a good time at that clubhouse. There was a bowling alley in the basement. We girls weren't allowed down there. It was segregated at the time. The billiard room and pool hall were for boys, too. It was built for the men at the mine, not the women or girls, you know, but we were allowed in the reading room. The company also built a clubhouse at the Baltic.

Downstairs there was also shower baths and the like that men could go. There was no plumbing around in the neighborhood so they couldn't have baths in their houses easily. They could take a shower every night if they wanted to and take a bath. And only on Thursday afternoons was it given over to the ladies. We took our baths every Thursday.

We used the reading room. There was a piano, a record player and lots of magazines. Back then we could sit and talk. Once in a while we were allowed to have a dance. No drinking was allowed anyplace. We used to have the lyceum courses come around. They were a group of traveling entertainers and we bought season tickets. We also had the Chautauqua. We did have a lot of entertainment in a way. We had a theater in Iron River—the Cozy, they called it. There was one in Stambaugh, too. We didn't have any radios—that was after in 1920 when WWJ started in Detroit. We didn't have a radio until 1925.

There is something interesting about this mine community at the time before the unions. They paid small wages, but they also provide you with a house, very cheap rent—for instance, our house had four rooms down and four rooms up and was five dollars a month rent. There was a big garden around it already fenced. We paid a dollar for our lights, a dollar for the water, and a dollar for the doctor. Eight dollars a month was all it cost for al of that. The unions called it paternalism.

D.B. 8/24/72

25

## MRS. WALTER HAWKE--*Housewife*

I came to Iron River from Germany when I was 13 years old, and the Main Street wasn't paved. There were those board sidewalks. There wasn't any lighting in the streets. I don't think there was electricity at that time. We had oil lamps at home with the chimneys. There were no cars. When they first came out it (stable/garage) was still at the Boyington House. One of the men, he was a bachelor—he never did marry, but he had a lot of money. He had interests in the Rogers mine and he was getting royalties. His name was William Schiebler. He bought a car and he gave us girls a ride—and oh! We wore those hats with the scarves over them like you've seen in pictures. We thought that was wonderful. I don't think it was a big car, just a small car, but we thought it was really something.

The men (at the mine) with their old square dinner pails with the coffee on the bottom and the coffee would be cold—they had no thermos bottles –and a tray for our sandwich and another tray for your dessert, and the cover. You'd carry that.

My husband was a pumpman at the Hiawatha towards the last. He worked three shifts, changing shifts each week, and he walked from Iron River to the mine every day. I worked at Kroms at the same time. I just kept on working because my daughter was in school and there wasn't too much to do. I managed to do my work.

We had lumberjacks here too. The town was full of them. They had lumber camps. It was either in the mine or in the woods. There was one saloon on top of the other. The Main Street was all saloons and there were hardly any stores. There was one hardware store and that was Quirt's. On both side of Main Street it was mostly all saloons. And the lumberjacks would be sitting outside and /laughs/. But I don't think there was much fighting. They all behaved themselves. They'd come to town when they had payday. They'd get drunk and spend all their money and go back to camp.

We had a Lutheran church that was up on Adams Street. There was no Christian Science church at that time. There was a Methodist church and the Episcopalian church. And there was a German Lutheran church in Stambaugh. That was all those days except the Catholic church, St. Agnes. One tragedy we had was when Father Lenhart was killed. He was murdered. This man's wife was working as a housekeeper for the Father. Lenhart was German and he spoke it. There was a Presbyterian church, too where the new church is now.

The people who were bosses in the mines had much influence in town. They used to tell you how to vote, too. And if you didn't vote right, you'd lose your job. That's true. I'm speaking from experience. After a while that changed so they couldn't do that. When they got the union in here, it changed. But they used to tell you.

(Unions, here) Ho, ho union. In the mine they put you wherever they wanted you and you went or else. Your wages were low. I really don't know what year they organized. But I remember the times when I voted and they'd tell you to vote so and so, the party.

D.B.  5/1974

## LYDIA KNEEBONE--*Location Living*

I came to Iron River at 16 years of age from National Mine. My dad was working at the Davidson Mine and boarding at Robert's boarding house at the J & L Location. The mines were all working so a man could hold 2 or 3 jobs at one time. Captain Sleeman would hire the 16 year old boys to drive mules and work on surface. They had mules underground then. I remember carrying dinner buckets to the J & L dry and seeing men stretched out on the floor, passed out from sulphur fumes. Me and a girl friend went down in the J & L one evening with two young men. We weren't afraid then.

We worked in the boarding house from morning until around six o'clock for $12 a month. There was a lot of rooms to clean. They also had a candy store and poolroom.

The cows had big bells. They would have to get up at night to chase them away. Mrs. Alto, a Finnish family, had cows. We used to go over and carry milk home in open pails, never thinking about germs. We never knew there was such a thing as germs! And we sure never needed a doctor.

When the strike was on at the Copper Country, we were always having new men come in. So we used to go up to the store and watch the men coming up to get board. We'd pick out the ones we would like and then we would forget them all in fun. The young men used to help us to fill all the lamps with kerosene and wipe stacks of dishes for us and then ask for dates only to be turned down. All people were friendly and willing to help anyone.

There was a Sunday school and gathering place at the beginning of the J & L Street. They used to hold parties and ladies' aid meetings there. The late Dick Roberts and Uncle John Roberts preached there.

To go to town we used to walk across the caves from the J & L to the Davidson—you can't do that anymore because it's all caved, and from the Davidson up over Minckler Hill, past the fairgrounds and across a wooden bridge over the river. We'd come out around Vantaggi's somewhere. And there were no lights. You had to guess your way.

Once we had a peddler came out walking from Iron River with a suitcase of watches and rings. By the time he got through showing them to the men, he didn't have much left. They would buy a few things and help themselves to the rest and he didn't dare say anything when he left, as the room was full of men.

Nolingberg's bakery came every morning to deliver bread, jellyrolls and sweets. And the Mercantile teamster used to come with wagon and team of horses.

At one time we had 42 boarders. We used to fix their three tiered aluminum dinner pails. And if we had a boy friend, he always got extra food and if he liked extra sugar in his tea, he got it. Some of the men would stop on the way home from work and get beer in the bottom of the dinner pail. That spoiled many pans of dishwater!

One day my girl friend made dates with everyone of the boarders that asked her, but she picked El (Mrs. Kneebone's husband to be). I wasn't going with him then. All the others were waiting at the washhouse door. She gave El the signal and he came into the house. They sneaked out the other entrance of the house and left the rest waiting.

It was so cold sometimes we would have to dress in bed, but we never minded it. Only one Christmas I remember me and Doris carried dinner pails without boots, a green Christmas.

I think I was at the boarding house two years. I was like one of the family. They sure were good to me.

D.B.  1/4/1973

**BILL HARRIS**--*Grandpa Bill gives a "kid's" description of the location*

My grandfather, Dad's father, was a mining captain and a house was built for him in Stambaugh. He was called down from Negaunee to help solve a quick sand problem at Tully mine. My grandmother put eight kids on the train, and came to live in Stambaugh too. Grandpa told me not to go underground. He had started as a shaft man, and ended up with bad arthritis.

My dad was a hoistman at the Davidson No. 1, and when I carried Mr. Olson's (lunch) pail, I would peek in the engine house door and watch him work at the hoist. He became safety first head later on.

The ladies in the location, the Cousin Jennies, Cousin Jack's wives, would make pasties every Thursday, and they would be delivered to the mine. Money would go to the Methodist Ladies Aid.

27

My grandmother was a sort of mid-wife in the location. She took care of the sick, etc. when there was a sign on the house, quarantined for Scarlet Fever, and other diseases.

I was born so small that the doctor didn't make out a birth certificate as he thought I wouldn't make it. My grandma thought I would. She held me for days, breathing in my mouth. When the doctor stopped three days after I was born to see how I was doing, he was surprised that the Harris kid was still around, and made out a birth certificate.

When we weren't doing our chores, such as sawing wood, chopping wood, hoeing the garden, picking weeds, helping Dad, or some of the other things we had to do, Bob and I, just eleven months apart, still had to work.

It seems that the kids in the location were just a few years apart. Most of the women were young and the babies just kept on coming! Families had three or four or five or six kids, and mostly only a year apart. We had enough kids to have a baseball team. Each location had a team and we all played each other.

The Davidson boys needed a field, so we went to work to build one behind Hans Anderson's house. The water pumped from the mine ran just behind the railroad tracks, so we had to build the field north of that. With wheelbarrow, shovels, picks, rakes, and all those tools, it took us two summers to finish it. But, still even then, it wasn't completely done. There was a large boulder by first base. We dug around it for about six hours and got down about four feet into the ground. The rock was getting bigger, so we filled in the hole, and used it for the first base!

We didn't have a real baseball, so Uncle Eldred gave us some tape. We had enough to wrap around and around until we had ourselves a spongy tape ball. No home runs.

We had a skating rink north of the location. The men built a trough that could be blocked off and the water from the mine would flood the rink. And then when the block was taken out of the trough, the water would stop filling the rink. We had the clamp-on skates that had to be tightened with a pair of pliers. But, even if we wore them as tight as we could get them, they would still come off. Playing crack the whip was the most fun. The water from the mine was high in sulfur, so our clothes took a beating. Kept Ma busy patching though!

The yards all had fences because herds of cows would stray by. They would be rounded up in time and taken home. We would try and catch one or two and ride them if we could. The Village put up a cow pound, and the owners of the cows would have to pay a dollar to get them out. We watched Gust Anderson, the pound manager, get into fights when Gust wouldn't let the men's cows go if they didn't have the money to pay him a dollar.

The mine had two horses, Tom and Jerry. We would try to corner them behind Kneebone's barn and jump on for a ride. I was thrown one time, and almost broke my arm. The horses were used at the mine, and would haul coal to our houses for five dollars a ton. As no one had any money, it would be charged to the mining company to be paid when and if the mines started.

Sometimes we would have a real treat when Dad would put us in the Model T and take us to Iron Lake swimming…We thought that it would be a good idea to build a raft and diving board at the North end of Iron Lake. We took lumber from the mine and hauled it piece by piece out to the lake. We had one problem: We had to go through a farm, Hemeleski's. There was a mean bull in the pasture, so we solved that by drawing straws. The one that got the short straw would run out in the field and when the bull was chasing him, we would haul our lumber across the field. It sure took us a lot of trips. We did build the raft, though, and it lasted for a few years.

One time there was a note at the mine that said that all the location boys were to go to the hall for an Audubon bird meeting. When the superintendent or his wife gave notice, you have better do just what they wanted. We showed up at the Hall wondering what it was all about. We hid our slingshots outside the Hall. We had to sing songs such as "Tweet, tweet, tweet, how the birdies sing". We were also told the importance of our feathered friends. On the way home, one of the boys shot some birds with his slingshot!

We didn't have a lot of money to buy things when I was a kid, so my friends and I made most of the things, which we played. We made our slingshots out of maple crotch in a small tree that we shaped a year before. We would make our own kites by getting cedar from the mine and cutting the kite frame with our knives. We'd mix flour and water to make glue, and we used newspaper to cover the whole works. It was hard to find string, but somehow we managed.

The Davidson Location houses were moved because of subsiding ground from mining in that area. The Village Hall was torn down in the 90's. My memories as a boy, raised in the late twenties and thirties have, of course dimmed, but I have tried to put down a few of them.

2000

## MURIEL HANSON BEAULIER

My grandfather was the first miner killed in the Tobin Mine in Crystal Falls, Michigan in 1908. He fell out of the cage as it was lowered down into the mine. He was 33 years old.

His name was Henry Freeman and he was born April 15, 1875, in Rakio, Starfurstendarmet, Vora (the Swedish part of Finland).

He was survived by his wife, Anna Lisa (Kullas) Freeman and three children, Edgar, Ellen and Irene.

2001

## WALTER BALL JR--*My father's accident*

My father, Walter Ball, Sr. got his first job in the mines sometime in 1941. Prior to that he cut pulp with an axe and bucksaw to support his family. He was hired at the Buck Mine through the influence of his good friend, "Windy Bill" Gollakner.

Over the years, he worked also at the Kinney, Bengal and Zimmerman mines. Finally taking a job at the Book Mine since we lived in Alpha.

As the open pit at the Book Mine began to peter out North Range Mining Co. began to sink a shaft. My father and his partner, Toisto Lehto worked on one of the shifts.

They went down and came to the surface in what was called a "bucket" as opposed to a "cage" or "skip".

One wintry day they came to the surface for lunch and on the way down the guides for the bucket became stuck and the hoistman didn't know it so the line kept playing out. The bucket broke free and both men were thrown onto a plank platform at what was to be one of the working levels of the mine. My father was unconscious and was hanging with his head out into the shaft and a solid grip on the plank platform. His partner couldn't pull him away and since they were near the bottom of the shaft, he pushed him down to the bottom. The alternative was my father being decapitated when the bucket finally reached them.

His partner then rang to the hoistman to stop the bucket but he was a little too late. My father landed on a pile of dirt on the bottom of the shaft in a sitting position. The bucket continued down and began pressing on his shoulders. He regained consciousness hearing his ribs being broken before he passed out again.

He awoke in the emergency room of the Crystal Falls Municipal Hospital with several broken ribs, some cracked vertebrae, and several wrenched knees. He was in a body cast for over six months.

He did recover and never complained of these injuries ever interfering with his fishing or hunting.

2001

**ALPHA**

**Location:** Crystal Falls, Iron Co., Mich. SE-SE Sec 11 and SW-SW Sec 12-T42N-R33W
**Description:** Explored in early eighties, but no record of shipments until 1903.
**Ore:** Soft, red, non-bessemer.   **Interests:** Inland Steel Co.   **Shipments:** 1903 -- 1,370 Tons
**Railroad:** C & N W   **Port:** Escanaba, Mich.

**ARMENIA**

**Location:** Crystal Falls, Iron Co., Mich. E ½ - SE Sec 23 - T43N - R32W
**Description:** Opened 1889; shipped through 1914, except 1891-1894, 1896-1900, and 1908-1909, Formerly operated by Corrigan McKinney & Co. Also known as Angus Smith or Smith mine. Lease surrendered in 1914.
**Ore:** Soft, Red, high phosphorus, Crushed, Grade shipped, 1913: Armenia.
**Mining Co.:** Corrigan, McKinney & Co (formerly)   **Shipments:** 1889-1914 -- 713,395 Tons
**Railroad:** C & N W and C M St P & P   **Port:** Escanaba, Mich.

**BAKER**

**Location:** Stambaugh, Iron Co., Mich. S $\frac{1}{2}$-SW and W $\frac{1}{2}$-SE Sec 31 - T43N - R34W
**Description:** Opened 1909; shipped continuously through 1915 except 1912. Formerly operated by Corrigan McKinney & Co.; later by Hanna Iron Ore Co.
**Ore:** Soft, red, high phosphorus. Crushed. Grade shipped, 1916: Baker.
**Mining Co.:** Hanna Iron Ore Co.   **Agent:** The M.A. Hanna Co.
**Shipments:** 1909-1915 -- 267,107 Tons   **Railroad:** C & N W   **Port:** Escanaba, Mich.

**BATES**

**Location:** Iron River, Iron Co., Mich. Includes Bates, W $\frac{1}{2}$-NW Sec 19 (i.e. west half of former Bates lease), and Johnson, N $\frac{1}{2}$-SW and part of S $\frac{1}{2}$-SW Sec 19 - T43N - R34W
**Description:** Opened 1910; has shipped every year. Formerly operated by Bates Iron Co.; later by Hannah Iron Ore Co. Mine closed in 1947. Worked by stoping method. Depth, 2,040 ft. No production from Johnson lease, acquired in 1947.
**Ore:** Soft, yellow, high phosphorus. Crushed. Grade shipped, 1947: Weir.
**Mining Co.:** Hanna Iron Ore Co.   **Agent:** The M.A. Hanna Co.
**Shipments:** 1915-1947 -- 4,054,666 Tons   **Railroad:** C & N W   **Port:** Escanaba, Mich.

**BALKAN-JUDSON**

**Location:** Alpha, Iron Co., Mich. NE-NW, S ½-NW and N ½-SW Sec 13 - T42N - R33W. Includes Alpha, NE-NW; Longyear, SE-NW; and McGovern, NE-SW Sec 13. Formerly included Mastodon, NE Sec 13

**Description:** Judson mine first opened in 1913 and the Balkan in 1915. Formerly separate operations but connected later and all ore produced through Judson shaft. Operated by Balkan Mining Co. until December 31, 1935, when lease surrendered to fee owners. Worked by stoping and slicing. Depth, 710 ft. Mastodon Mine formerly part of Balkan-Judson; shipped 1882 through 1896. Stockpile shipment in 1942 by Pittsburgh Coke and Iron Co.

**Ore:** Soft, Red, high phosphorus and manganiferous. Partially crushed. Grades shipped, 1935: Osana and Judson.

**Interests**: Inland Steel Co. (NE-NW, SW-NW, SE-NW and NE-SW Sec 13 - T42N - R33W only). Unknown - NW-SW and NE Sec 13 - T42N - R33W.

**Shipments:** Balkan-Judson    1914-1935    3,994,484 Tons
              Mastodon        1882-1942      447,315
              Total           1882-1942    4,441,799

**Railroad:** C & N W and C M St P & P    **Port:** Escanaba, Mich.

## BENGAL-TULLY - CANNON

**Location:** Stambaugh, Iron Co., Mich. N ½-SE (Bengal), S ½-SE (Tully) Sec 36 - T43N - R35W and NW-SW Sec 31 - T43N - R35W

**Description:** Bengal opened 1913 and shipped every year, except 1931-1932 and 1936. Operated by the Verona Mining Co. (Pickands Mather & Co., Agent). Acquired by the Hanna Iron Ore Co. in February 1944 and shipped in 1949-1950. Tully opened in 1909, shipped 1910-1911, 1913-1919, 1921-1922 and 1926. Formerly operated by Corrigan McKinney Steel Co., and later acquired by Hanna Iron Ore Co. Shipped in 1949-1950. Bengal worked by stoping and slicing methods. Depth, 875 ft. Tully worked by milling method. Upon completion of the new shaft, this mine was called Cannon.

**Ore:** Soft, Red, high phosphorus. Part crushed. Grade shipped, 1950: Weir.

**Mining Co.:** Hanna Iron Ore Co.    **Agent:** The M.A. Hanna Co.

**Shipments:** Bengal   1913-1944   5,470,357 Tons
                      1949-1950    <u>201,466</u> Tons
         Bengal Total       5,671,823
         Tully    1910-1926   1,151,623
                  1949-1950       1,594
         Tully Total        1,153,217
   Bengal-Tully Total   1910-1950   6,825,040

**Railroad:** C & N W    **Port:** Escanaba, Mich.

33

**CANNON**

**Location:** Stambaugh, Iron Co. , Mich.N ¹/₂-SE (Bengal),S ¹/₂-SE (Tully) Sec 36T43N-R35W and NW-SW Sec 31-T43N-R35W
**Description:** Formerly Bengal-Tully. Opened 1953 and Closed 1962. Depth 1708 Feet.
**Production:** 1953-1963 4,796,663 included in Bengal-Tully total.

**BETA**

**Location**: Iron River, Iron Co., Mich. NW-SW Sec 26-T43N-R35W
**Description:** Opened 1886; shipped in 1886-1887 and 1891. Closed in 1887 but shipped 1891 and 1941-1942 from stockpile. Exhausted. This property later included in Nanaimo. 1941-1942 Shipments made by Pittsburgh Coke & Iron Co.   **Shipments:** 1886-1942-27,156 Tons
**Railroad:** C & N W   **Port:** Escanaba, Mich.

## BOOK

**Location:** Alpha, Iron Co., Mich. NE and NE-NW Sec 12-T42N-R23W
**Description:** Opened in 1942. First shipment in 1943. Has shipped every year since. Operated by North Range Mining Co. Originally opened as an open pit, now worked as an underground mine by stoping method. Depth, 500 ft.
**Ore:** Soft, red, high phosphorus. Grade shipped, 1950: Book
**Mining Co.:** North Range Mining Co.     **Shipments:** 1943-1950-1,349,360 Tons. 1951-1957-855,095
Total: 2,205,055     **Railroad:** C & N W     **Port:** Escanaba, Mich.

## BORLAND

*(No Photo Available)*

**Location:** Gaastra, Iron Co., Mich. N ½-NW Sec 6-T42N-R34W
**Description:** An old exploration, held as a reserve.     **Interests:** The Verona Mining Co.
**Agent:** Pickands Mather & Co.

1912

## BRISTOL (BRISTAL)-YOUNGSTOWN

**Location:** Crystal Falls, Iron Co., Mich. Bristol, E ½ SE Sec 19 and Youngstown, W ½ SW Sec 20-T43N-R23W

**Description:** Bristol was opened 1892;shipped through 1934, except 1894-1898. Operated by Bristol Mining Co. with Oglebay, Norton & Co. as sales and operating agent. Mining lease surrendered April 12, 1933. Shipments from stockpile completed in 1934. Once known as Claire mine. The Bristol together with NW-SW Sec 20 (part of Youngstown) was operated as Bristol-Youngstown mine by Oglebay, Norton & Co. from 1926 to 1933. The Youngstown was leased by Inland Steel Co. from Oliver Iron Mining Co. in 1949, reopened together with Brisol as Bristol-Youngston, with shipments in 1950. Worked by shrinkage and sub-level stoping systems. Depth, 1,525 ft.

**Ore:** Coarse,brown, high phosphorus, manganiferous. Crushed. Grades shipped, 1950:Bristol

**Mining Co.:** Inland Steel Co.

**Shipments:**

| | | |
|---|---|---|
| 1890- | 6,844 Tons (Manganate)* | |
| 1892-1934 | 8,614,235 | |
| 1950-1967 | 9,352,578 | |
| 1968-1969 | 634,511 | |
| Total | 18,713,186 | |

**Railroad:** C & N W and C M St P & P    **Port:** Escanaba, Mich.

*Note- In 1890 a shipment of 6,844 tons called "Manganate" was made from this property. Probably made by a Mr. Roberts who was active in that property until it was taken over by Oglebay, Norton & Co. in 1899.*

36

**BUCK GROUP**

**Location:**  Caspian, Iron Co., Mich. Includes Baltic, W ½-W ½ Sec 7: Berkshire, NW-SW and SW-NW Sec 6; Bucks, S ½ -SW Sec 6; De Grasse, NE Sec 7: Zimmerman, E ½-NW Sec 7 – T42N-R34W: and Fogarty SE-SE Sec 1-T42N-R35W

**Description:**  The present Buck Group includes the Buck mine, which in itself has been a group operation since 1922 embracing the Baltic, Fogarty, and Buck properties; the Berkshire mine (not including the Cottrell, NE-SE Sec 1, which was part of Berkshire before 1934); the Zimmerman mine and the De Grasse, operated through the Zimmerman shaft. (See Buck, Berkshire, Cottrell, De Grasse and Zimmerman descriptions for records of individual mines.)

**Ore:**  Soft, red-brown, high phosphorus. Grades shipped, 1950: Osana and Osana Two.

**Mining Co.:**  The Verona Mining Co.      **Agent:** Pickands Mather & Co.

**Shipments:**

| | | |
|---|---|---|
| Baltic | 1901-1950 | 2,574,216 Tons |
| Buck | 1922-1950 | 5,412,657 |
| Fogarty | 1907-1949 | 1,515,721 |
| Berkshire | 1908-1950 | 4,189,586 |
| Zimmerman | 1901-1950 | 3,609,727 |
| De Grasse | 1950-1967 | 3,796,380 |
| Total | | 21,098,287 |

37

SMUGGLER MINE NO6
PALATKA, MICH. 1908

17735 FOGERTY MINE, PALATKA, MICH.

## BERKSHIRE

**Location:**  Caspian, Iron Co., Mich.  SW-NW and NW-SW Sec 6–T42N–R34W
Description:  Opened 1908; shipped every year through 1930, except 1913 and 1941-1942.  Shipped from stockpile 1936-1937.  After 1916 and prior to 1934, included Cottrell mine. Previously operated by Brule Mining Co. (Oglebay. Norton & Co., Agent).  The Corry "40", NE-SW Sec6-42-34, was operated by the Brule through the Berkshire mine shaft. Berkshire later taken over by Youngstown Mines Corp. and subsequently by The Verona Mining Co.  This property is now part of the Buck Group.  Worked by top-slicing and sublevel caving methods.
**Ore:**  Soft, red-brown, high phosphorus.  Constituent of grade shipped, 1950: Osana.
**Mining Co.:**  The Verona Mining Co.    **Agent:**  Pickands Mather & Co.
**Shipments:**  1908-1950   4,189,586 Tons  (includes Corry "40") included in Buck total.
**Railroad:**  C & N W    **Port:**  Escanaba, Mich.

## BUCK
*(No Photo Available)*

**Location:**  Caspian, Iron Co., Mich. Baltic, W ½ -W ½ Sec 7; Buck, S ½ -SW Sec 6- T42N-R34W: and Fogarty, SE-SE Sec 1-T42N-R35W

**Description:**  Baltic opened in 1901, Fogarty in 1907 and Buck in 1922, and have formed one operation since.  The Baltic has shipped every year since opening except 1919-1920, 1932, 1934-1936.  The Buck has shipped every year except 1932, and the Fogarty every year except 1943, 1945-1947 and 1950. Worked by stoping and slicing.  Depth, 753 feet. Now part of Buck Group.

**Ore:**  Soft, red-brown, high phosphorus. Part crushed. Grades shipped, 1950: Osana and Osana Two.

**Mining Co.:**  The Verona Mining Co.      **Agent:**  Pickands Mather & Co.

**Shipments**:  Baltic      1901-1950    2,574,216 Tons
Buck        1922-1950    5,412,657
Fogarty   1907-1949    1,515,721
**Total**      1901-1950    9,502,594    included in Buck Group

**Railroad:**  C & N W    **Port:**  Escanaba, Mich.

## CORRY "40"
*(No Photo Available)*

**Location:**  Stambaugh, Iron Co., Mich.  NE-SW Sec 6-T42N-R34W

**Description:**  Shipped 1922-1928.  Formerly operated through Berkshire mine shaft by Brule Mining Co. (Oglebay, Norton & Co., Agent).  Shipments are included with Berkshire.  Worked by stoping method. Depth, 400 feet.

**Ore:**  Soft, red, high phosphorus.    **Mining Co.:**  Brule Mining Co,  (formerly)

**Agent:**  Oglebay, Norton & Co. (formerly)

**Shipments:**  1922-1928   67,616 Tons (included in Berkshire shipments)

**Railroad:**  C & N W      **Port:**  Escanaba, Mich.

## DE GRASSE
*(No Photo Available)*

**Location:** Gaastra, Iron Co., Mich.  NE Sec7-T42N-R34W
**Description:** Former reserve property of The Verona Mining Co. (Pickands Mather & Co., Agent) which was acquired in 1943.  The first shipment was made from this property in 1950.  It is operated with the Zimmerman as part of the Buck Group.
**Ore:** Soft, red-brown, high phosphorus, Part crushed.  Grades shipped. 1950: Osana and Osana Two.
**Mining Co.:** The Verona Mining Co.    **Agent:** Pickands Mather & Co.
**Shipments:** 1950    28,682 Tons – included in the Buck Group
**Railroad:** C & N W    **Port:** Escanaba, Mich.

## ZIMMERMAN

**Location:** Gaastra, Iron Co., Mich.  E ½ NW Sec 7-T42N-R34W
**Description**: Opened 1907; shipped 1098-1949, except years 1921,1933 and 1938-1941. 1937 shipment from stockpile and 1944-1945 shipments partly from stockpile by The M. A. Hanna Co. Formerly operated by Hanna Iron Ore Co. Acquired in 1944 by The Verona Mining Co. and since operated as part of the Buck Group.
**Ore:** Soft, red, high phosphorus. Crushed. Constituent of grade shipped, 1950:Osana.
**Mining Co.:** The Verona Mining Co.    **Agent:** Pickands Mather & Co.
**Shipments:** 1907-1950 3,609,727 Tons included in Buck Group    **Railroad:** C & N W
**Port:** Escanaba, Mich.

**BUCKHOLTZ**

**Location:**  Iron River, Iron Co., Mich. SE Sec 27-T43N-R35W
**Description:**  A reserve property on which considerable drilling has been done since 1948.
**Interests:**  Mineral Mining Co.

**CARDIFF**

**Location:**  Iron River, Iron Co., Mich. E ½ -NE, N ½ -SE and SW-NE Sec 22-T43N-R35W. Includes Keweenaw, N ½-SE and SW-NE and Mc Govern, E ½ -NE.
**Description:**  Opened 1919; shipped 1922 and 1923. Formerly operated by Wickwire Mining Co., a subsidiary of Wickwire Steel Co.; now held by Hanna Iron Ore Co. and is a part of Homer mine. Worked by sub-level stoping method.
**Ore:**  Medium hard, red-brown, high phosphorus. Grade shipped, 1922:Homer.
**Mining Co.:**  Hanna Iron Ore Co.    **Agent:**  The M. A. Hanna Co.
**Shipments:**  1922-1923  144,415 Tons (included in Homer)    **Port:**  Escanaba, Mich.

42

**CARPENTER**

**Location:** Crystal Falls, Iron Co., Mich. N $^1/_2$ -SW Sec 31-T43N-R32W
**Description:** Opened 1913; shipped every year 1914-1928. Formerly operated by Hanna Furnace Co. (Hollister Mining Co.). Worked by slicing and stoping method.
**Ore:** Hard and soft, red, high phosphorus. Grade shipped, 1928: Carpenter.
**Mining Co.:** Hollister Mining Co. (formerly)     **Agent:** The M. A. Hanna Co. (formerly)
**Shipments:** 1914-1928  2,735,452 Tons     **Railroad:** C & N W and C M St P & P
**Port:** Escanaba, Mich.

**CASPIAN**

**Location:** Caspian, Iron Co., Mich. NE Sec 1-T42N-R35W
**Description:** Opened 1903; shipped every year 1903-1937 except 1921 and 1932. Operated by The Verona Mining Co. Worked by stoping and slicing. Depth, 539 ft. Now flooded.
**Ore:** Soft, red, brown, high phosphorus. Some are crushed. Constituent of grade shipped, 1937: Osana Mixture.     **Mining Co.:** The Verona Mining Co.
**Agent:** Pickands Mather & Co.     **Shipments:** 1903-1937  6,623,320 Tons
**Railroad:** C & N W     **Port:** Escanaba, Mich.

CASPIAN MINE
L5619

CASPIAN IRON MINE NEAR IRON RIVER, MICH.

CASPIAN MINE
No 2 STAMBAUGH, MICH.
1908

E. AMMERMANN,
IRON RIVER, MICH.

45

Cayia Mine (July 1951) -- This short-lived mine located on M-69 East was beset by water problems from the beginning and did not prove successful. Seated in front are Clinton Davis, Louis Depotie, John Schmidt, Joseph Lesandrini, Nels Koskela, and Charles Van Troba. The second row includes Joe Kusmitch, Pete Mitchell, Rudy Anderson, Andrew Vicenzi, Gust Van Develde, Waino Korkiamaki, Jim Silva and Ernest Schaal. Standing are Richard Marstead, Harold Moyle, A. Johnson, Ed Wickstrom, Leonard Grattan, Fred Silvensky, and Bud Aliprandini. In the background are Ralph Trepasso and Onnie Salo.

## CAYIA

**Location:** Crystal Falls, Iron Co., Mich. NE-SW, NW-SE and SE-NW Sec 26-T43N-R32W
**Description:** A reserve property, once known as D. M. & M., originially held by Jones & Laughlin Steel Corp. Now under lease to Inland Steel Co. Under development in 1951 for first production in 1952.
**Interests:** Inland Steel Co.     **Shipments:** 1953  44,492 Tons

## CHATHAM

**Location:** Stambaugh, Iron Co., Mich. NE-SE Sec 35-T43N-R35W
**Description:** Opened 1907; shipped every year through 1920. Formerly operated by Brule Mining Co., now by Hanna Iron Ore Co. Now a part of Hiawatha No. 1
**Ore:** Soft, brown, high phosphorus. Some crushed. Grade shipped, 1920: Chatham.
**Mining Co.:** Hanna Iron Ore Co.     **Agent:** The M. A. Hanna Co.
**Shipments:** 1907-1920  1,381,175 Tons (included in Hiawatha No. 1)
**Railroad:** C & N W     **Port:** Escanaba, Mich.

**CHICAGOAN**

**Location:** Iron River, Iron Co., Mich. NW-NE, S ½ -NE and NE-SE Sec 26-T43N-R34W
**Description:** Opened 1909; shipped 1911-1922. Operated by Monroe Iron Mining Co. (Rogers Brown Iron Co.). Now held by Hanna Iron Ore Co., as a reserve. Worked by stoping method.
**Ore:** Hard, red, high phosphorus and manganiferous. Crushed. Grades shipped, 1919: Chicagoan and Mangrove. **Interests:** Hanna Iron Ore Co. **Agent:** The M. A. Hanna Co.
**Shipments:** 1911-1922 1,234,339 Tons **Railroad:** C & N W and C M St P & P
**Port:** Escanaba, Mich.

**COLUMBIA**

**Location:** Crystal Falls, Iron Co., Mich. NW Sec 31-T43N-R32W
**Description:** Shipped 1882-1905 and 1941-1950. Formerly held by Corrigan Mc Kinney Steel Co.; now by Republic Steel Corp. Columbia ore taken through Tobin shaft. Tobin and Columbia together comprise old Sheldon and Shafer property. Worked by sub-level stoping. Depth, 1,783 ft.
**Mining Co.:** Republic Steel Corp.
**Shipments:** 1882-1905    944,795 Tons
                      1941-1950  <u>3,363,806</u>
     Total    1882-1950  4,308,601
**Railroad:** C & N W and C M St P & P    **Port:** Escanaba. Mich.

## CORTLAND
*(No Photo Available)*

**Location:** Stambaugh, Iron Co., Mich. E ½-SE Sec 34-T43N-R35W
**Description:** Opened 1912; shipped 1912-1914. Formerly operated by Wickwire Mining Co. (Wickwire Steel Co. Agent). SE-SE acquired by Hanna Iron Ore Co.
**Ore:** High phosphorus. Grade shipped, 1914: Cortland.
**Interests:** SE-SE Sec 34-T43N-R35W only    **Agent:** The M.A. Hanna Co.
**Shipments:** 1912-1914 52,148 Tons    **Railroad:** C & N W    **Port:** Escanaba, Mich.


## COTTRELL
*(No Photo Available)*

**Location:** Caspian, Iron Co., Mich. NE-SE Sec 1-T42N-R35W
**Description:** Opened in 1915 and shipped 1915-1916. Operated by the Brule Mining Co. (Oglebay, Norton & Co.). Later became a part of Berkshire operated by Youngstown Mines Corp. and subsequently by The Verona Mining Co. (Pickands Mather & Co.). Acquired in 1934 from Detroit and Marquette Land Co. by Hanna Iron Ore Co. and since held by it. The Verona Mining Co. has permit from the Hanna Co. to use the Cottrell mine in operating the Berkshire (in present Buck Group) which adjoins it. No shipments since 1916.
**Ore:** Soft, red brown, high phosphorus    **Interests:** Hanna Iron Ore Co.
**Agent:** The M. A. Hanna Co.    **Shipments:** 1915-1916 75,134 Tons
**Railroad:** C & N W    **Port:** Escanaba, Mich.

## CRYSTAL FALLS

**Location:** Crystal Falls, Iron Co., Mich. E ½-NE Sec 21-T43N-R32W
**Description:** Opened 1882; shipped every year through 1913, except 1883-1889, 1891-1894 and 1910. Formerly operated by Corrigan Mc Kinney & Co. Lease surrendered August 31,1913. Held by Inland Steel Co. since 1949.
**Ore:** Soft, brown, high phosphorus.    **Mining Co.:** Inland Steel Co.
**Shipments:** 1882-1913 1,744,015 Tons    **Railroad:** C & N W and C M St P & P
**Port:** Escanaba, Mich.

# DELPHIC
*(No Photo Available)*

**Location:** Alpha, Iron Co., Mich. NE-SW Sec 24-T42N-R33W
**Description:** Opened 1883; shipped 1883-1887 and 1896.
**Ore:** Soft, red, high phosphorus    **Shipments:** 1883-1896 33,770 Tons
**Railroads:** C & N W and C M St P & P    **Port:** Escanaba, Mich.

# DAVIDSON GROUP

**Location:** Iron River, Iron Co., Mich. Davidson No. 1, NE-NW Sec 23; Davidson No. 2; W ½ -SE Sec 14; Davison No. 3, SE-SE Sec 14; Barnett, SW Sec 13; and SE-SW Sec 14 (part of Forbes) all in T43N-R35W
**Description:** Opened 1911; has shipped every year except 1932. Operated by Davidson Ore Mining Co. through 1940; by Pittsburgh Coke & Iron Co., 1941-1947. Leased by Pickands Mather & Co., January 1,1947. 1947 shipments from active operation by Pickands Mather & Co., and from stockpile by Pittsburgh Coke & Co. Worked by back stoping and caving method.
Davidson No. 1: 950 ft. deep.
Davidson No. 2: 445 ft. deep.
Davidson No. 3: 900 ft. deep.
Barnett; held as reserve, SE-SW Sec 14 (part of Forbes) was acquired by Pickands Mining Co. (Pickands Mather & Co., Agent) in 1947 and used as the site for the Davidson shaft.
**Ore:** Soft, yellow, high phosphorus. Grade shipped, 1950: Sterling.
**Mining Co.:** Pickands Mining Co.    **Agent:** Pickands Mather & Co.
**Shipments:** 1911-1937 4,293,612 Tons
                1937-1950 2,993,420
                1950-1953 <u>909,982</u>
                Total       8,197,014    Closed in 1953

# DAVIDSON NO. 4

**Location:** Iron River, Iron Co., Mich. W ½ -SW Sec 14-T43N-R35W
**Description:** Opened 1912; shipped in 1913 and 1917-1921. Exhausted. Once known as Wapama.
**Mining Co.:** Davidson Ore Mining Co. (formerly)
**Shipments:** 1913-1921 128,599 Tons    **Railroad:** C & N W    **Port:** Escanaba, Mich.

Davidson Mine--Mineral Hills 1913

Davidson No. 2.    IRON RIVER, Mich.

**DELTA**

**Location:**  Iron River, Iron Co., Mich. W ¹/₂-W ¹/₂ Sec 25-T43N-R35W
**Description:**  Opened 1920; shipped 1920-1925, except 1922. Formerly operated by Delta Mining Co.
**Ore:**  High phosphorus. Grade shipped, 1925: Delta. **Mining Co.:**  Delta Mining Co. (formerly)
**Shipments:**  1920-1925   95,759 Tons    **Railroad:**  C & N W
**Port:**  Escanaba, Mich.

**DUNN**

**Location:**  Crystal Falls, Iron Co., Mich.  W ¹/₂-NE Sec 1-T42N-R33W
**Description:**  Opened 1887; shipped every year through 1915, except 1900-1901 and 1904. Formerly operated by Corrigan Mc Kinney & Co.; later held by Corrigan Mc Kinney Steel Co. Acquired by Republic Steel Corp., September 30, 1935. Lease surrendered February 29, 1936. Worked by stoping methods.
**Ore:**  Soft, reddish-brown, high phosphorus. Crushed. Grade shipped, 1915: Dunn
**Mining Co.:**  Corrigan Mc Kinney & Co. (formerly)
 **Shipments:**  1887-1915  2,208,511    **Railroad:**  C & N W    **Port:**  Escanaba, Mich.

Jones & Laughlin, Forbes Mine.   IRON RIVER, Mich.

## FORBES

**Location:**  Iron River, Iron Co., Mich. NE-SW Sec 14-T43N-R36W. Formerly included SE-SW Sec 14-T43N-R35W

**Description:**  Opened 1912 has shipped every year beginning 1913, except 1917-1919, 1921-1922, 1931-1933 and 1940-1942. Operated at one time by Jones & Laughlin Ore Co. Acquired by North Range Mining Co. April 1, 1935. Operated 1941-1946 by Pittsburgh Coke & Iron Co. Worked by stoping method. Depth, 475 ft. SE-SW Sec 14 acquired by Pickands Mining Co. (Pickands Mather & Co., Agent) in 1947 and the property is used as the site for the Davidson shaft. SE-SW Sec 14 included in Davidson Group.

**Ore:**  Soft, yellow, high phosphorus.    **Mining Co.:**  Pittsburg Coke & Iron Co.

**Shipments:**  1913-1937  2,090,835 Tons
             1938-1946   <u>192,987</u>
             Total         2,283,822

**Railroad:**  C & N W and C M St P & P    **Port:**  Escanaba, Mich.

1909

**FORTUNE LAKE**

**Location:** Crystal Falls, Iron Co., Mich. SW-NE and NE-NE Sec 26, N ¹/₂ -NW Sec 25 and S ¹/₂ -SW Sec 24-T43N-R33W
**Description:** Explored 1915 and 1920 by Fortune Lake Mining Co. (Oglebay, Norton & Co., Agent). Considerable drilling done and a shaft sunk to a depth of 277 ft. Held as a reserve; opened by stripping for underground milling operation.
**Ore:** Reported to be semi-hard, high in phosphorus,averaging about 2.0 % manganese, dried.
**Mining Co.:** Fortune Lake Mining Co.    **Agent:** Oglebay, Norton & Co.
**Shipments:** None    **Railroad:** C M St P & P    **Port:** Escanaba, Mich.
**Reopened:** Operated as an open pit mine 1953-1956 by Pickands Mather Co.
**Productions:** 1953-1956  1,175,341 Tons.

**GENESEE  (Ethel)**
*(No Photo Available)*

**Location:** Crystal Falls, Iron Co., Mich. SE Sec 30, W ¹/₂ -SW and NE-SW Sec 29-T43N-R32W
**Description:** Opened 1902; shipped through 1935, except 1908, 1913-1914, 1916-1927 and 1931. Once known as Ethel. Formerly operated by  Corrigan McKinney Steel Co. Acquired By Republic Steel Corp. in 1935 and lease surrendered February 29,1936. Depth, 860 ft.
**Ore:** Soft, reddish-brown, high phosphorus. Crushed. Grade shipped, 1935: Genesee.
**Mining Co.:** Republic Steel Corp. (formerly)    **Shipments:** 1902-1935  1,198,383 Tons
**Railroad:** C & N W and C M St P & P    **Port:** Escanaba, Mich.

53

## GIBSON

**Location:** Amasa, Iron Co., Mich. NW-NW Sec 15-T44N-R33W
**Description:** Opened 1885; shipped 1885-1887 and 1908-1911. Formerly operated by Rogers-Brown Ore Co. Leased in 1948 by North Range Mining Co. and Now included in Warner mine.
**Mining Co.:** North Range Mining Co. **Shipments:** 1885-1911 159,453 Tons
**Railroad:** C M St P & P **Port:** Escanaba, Mich.

## GREIG-KELLY-JACKSON
*(No Photo Available)*

**Location:** Iron River, Iron Co., Mich. Includes Greig, E $\frac{1}{2}$-E $\frac{1}{2}$ Sec 33 and Kelly-Jackson, SW-SE, SE-SW and SW-NE Sec 33-T43N-R35W
**Description:** A reserve property under lease by Inland Steel Co. since May 1948.
**Interests:** Inland Steel Co.

## HAGERMAN
*(No Photo Available)*

**Location:** Crystal Falls, Iron Co., Mich. SW-NE and NW-SE Sec 21-T43N-R32W
**Description:** A reserve property, formerly held by Corrigan McKinney Steel Co. and other interests. Now wholly owned by Republic Steel Corp. which has completed an exploratory drilling program.
**Interests:** Republic Steel Corp.

## HALF AND HALF
*(No Photo Available)*

**Location:** Unknown; no records except of production.
**Shipments:** 1889-1891  7,524 Tons

## HERSEL
*(No Photo Available)*

**Location:** Unknown; no records except of production.
**Shipments:** 1890  955 Tons

## GREAT WESTERN

**Location:** Crystal Falls, Iron Co., Mich. E ½-SW and SW-SE Sec 21-T43N-R32W
**Description:** Opened 1882; shipped through 1925, except 1885, 1894-1895, 1897, 1914, 1916, 1920-1921 and 1923-1924. Mine last operated in 1910; 300,00 tons accumulated stockpile was shipped in later years. Operated by Corrigan Mc Kinney Steel Co. Acquired by Republic Steel Corp. in 1935. Lease surrendered February 1936. Worked by stoping method. Depth, 1,250 ft.
**Ore:** Soft, reddish-brown, high phosphorus. Crushed. Grade shipped, 1925: Great Western
**Mining Co.:** Corrigan Mc Kinney Steel Co. (formerly)
**Shipments:** 1882-1925  2,296,739 Tons      **Railroad:** C & N W and C M St P & P
**Port:** Escanaba, Mich.

1911

## HEMLOCK

**Location:** Amasa, Iron Co., Mich. W ½ -SW Sec 4 –T44N-R33W

**Description:** Opened 1891; shipped every year through 1919, except 1894 and 1917. Stockpile shipment in 1938. Formerly operated by Hemlock River Mining Co. Lease surrendered. Worked by stoping method, Depth, 500 ft.

**Ore:** Hard, red, high phosphorus. Grade shipped, 1909: Hemlock.

**Mining Co.:** Hemlock River Mining Co. (formerly)    **Agent:** Pickands Mather & Co. (formerly)

**Shipments:** 1891-1919 2,125,681 Tons

| | |
|---|---|
| 1938 | <u>75</u> |
| Total | 2,125,756 |

**Railroad:** C & N W    **Port:** Escanaba, Mich.

## (HIAWATHA GROUP)

### BRULE (Hiawatha # 3)

**Location:** Stambaugh, Iron Co., Mich. NE-SW and NW-SE Sec 34-T43N-R35W

**Description:** Formerly operated by Brule Mining Co. (Oglebay, Norton & co.) Acquired by Hanna Iron Ore Co. in 1931 who made a small shipment from stockpile in 1936. Sometimes known as Hiawatha No. 3

**Ore:** Hard, red, high phosphorus. Grades shipped, 1936: Fink and Weir.

**Mining Co.:** Hanna Iron Ore Co.    **Agent:** The M. A. Hanna Co.

**Shipments:** 1936 4,200 Tons    **Railroads:** C & N W    **Port:** Escanaba, Mich.

(HIAWATHA GROUP - Cont.)

## HIAWATHA NO. 1

**Location:** Stambaugh, Iron Co., Mich W $\frac{1}{2}$-NE, NE-SW,S $\frac{1}{2}$ -SW and SE Sec 35-T43N-R35W. Includes NW-NE, part of former Wickwire; SW-NE, old Anna; S $\frac{1}{2}$ -SW, West Hiawatha; NE-SE, Chatham; SE-SE, Stegmiller; and NW-SE and NE-SW, North Hiawatha, all in Sec 35-T43N-R35W.
**Description:** Opened 1893; has shipped every year except 1894, 1896-1899 and 1907. Formerly operated by Munro Iron Mining Co.; later by Hanna Iron Ore Co. Worked by stoping method. Depth, 2,100 ft. For early history of Chatham see Chatham. North Hiawatha lease secured and property included in Hiawatha No. 1 in 1951.
**Ore:** Hard, red, high phosphorus. Crushed. Constituent of grade shipped, 1950: Weir.
**Mining Co.:** Hanna Iron Ore Co.    **Agent:** The M. A. Hanna Co.
**Shipments:** Hiawatha No. 1   1893-1950   8,502,729 Tons
                Chatham            1907-1920   1,381,175
                      Total         9,883,904
**Railroad:** C & N W    **Port:** Escanaba, Mich.

**HIAWATHA NO. 2**

**Location:** Caspian, Iron Co., Mich. NE and NE-NW Sec 2; NW Sec 1-T42N-R35W and SW-SW Sec 36-T43N-R35W. Includes Duff, E ½ -NE Sec 2; Dober, NW Sec 1-T42N-R35W and Isabella, SW-SW Sec 36-T43N-R35W

**Description:** The Dober, Duff and Isabella mines were operated as part of the Riverton Group (which see) by the Oliver Iron Mining Co. until taken into the Hiawatha No. 2 in 1935. The Hiawatha No. 2 was originally operated by American-Boston Mining Co.; now by Hanna Iron Ore Co. Worked by stoping method. Depth, 2,280 ft.

**Ore:** Hard, red, high phosphorus. Crushed. Constituent of grade shipped, 1950: Weir.

**Mining Co.:** Hanna Iron Ore Co.     **Agent:** The M. A. Hanna Co.

**Shipments:** 1935-1950   3,137.064 Tons
              1950-1966 <u>9,157,658</u>
              Total         12,294,722 Tons

**Railroad:** C& N W     **Port:** Escanaba, Mich.

HIAWATHA No. 2 MINE -- MENOMINEE RANGE

Hiawatha #1 - 1926

**HILLTOP**

*(No Photo Available)*

**Location:** Crystal Falls, Iron Co., Mich. SW-NW and Lot 3, equivalent to W ½-SW Sec 22-T43N-R32W

**Description:** Opened 1899; shipped 1899-1901, 1906, 1914 and 1917-1919. Operated by Oliver Iron Mining Co. until 1912; lease then assigned to Roberta Ore Co. Operated in 1914 by Cuyahoga Mining Co. and in 1917 by J. E. Thropp. Victoria, NW-NW Sec 22, was operated with Hilltop at one time, and any shipments from it are included with Hilltop.

**Ore:** Soft, red, high phosphorus.    **Shipments:** 1899-1919  98,202 Tons

**Railroad:** C & N W and C M St P & P    **Port:** Escanaba, Mich.

**HOLLISTER**

*(No Photo Available)*

**Location:** Crystal Falls, Iron Co., Mich. W ½-SW Sec 13-T43N-R32W

**Description:** Opened 1890; shipped 1890-1892, 1907-1911 and 1913-1914. Once operated by Oliver Iron Mining Co., later by Hollister Mining Co. Worked by stoping method.

**Ore:** Soft, red, high phosphorus. Grade shipped, 1910: Hollister

**Mining Co.:** Hollister Mining Co. (formerly)    **Agent:** The H. A. Hanna Co. (formerly)

**Shipments:** 1890-1914  143,117 Tons    **Railroad:** C & N W and C M St P & P

**Port:** Escanaba, Mich.

**HOPE**

*(No Photo Available)*

**Location:** Crystal Falls, Iron Co., Mich. E ½-SE Sec 27-T43N-R32W. Includes South Hope, SE-SE Sec 27 and Hope, NE-SE Sec 27.

**Description:** Opened 1892; shipped 1892-1893 and 1902-1903. NE-SE Sec 27 formerly operated by Hope Iron Mining Co. SE-SE Sec 27, known as South Hope. Was operated through Hope. Present Hope property once known as Wauneta and Blaney and once operated by Oliver Iron Mining Co.

**Ore:** Hard, red, high phosphorus.    **Mining Co.:** Hope Iron Mining Co.(formerly)

**Sales Agent:** Oglebay, Norton & Co.    **Shipments:** 1892-1903  28,530 Tons

**Railroad:** C & N W    **Port:** Escanaba, Mich.

**HOMER**

**Location:** Iron River, Iron Co., Mich. Homer, W ¹/₂-NW, NW-SW Sec 23-T43N-R35W; Cardiff, made up McGovern, E ¹/₂-NE and Keweenaw, N ¹/₂-SE and SW-NE Sec 22-T43N-R35W; Minckler, NE-SW and W ¹/₂ NW-SE Sec 23-T43N-R35W

**Description:** Opened 1914; shipped every year beginning 1915, except 1931-1932 and 1934. Formerly operated by Buffalo Iron Mining Co.; later by Hanna Iron Ore Co. Worked by sub-stoping method. Depth, 1,108 ft.

**Ore:** Medium red-brown, high phosphorus. Constituent of grade shipped, 1950:Weir.

**Mining Co.:** Hanna Iron Ore Co.    **Agent:** The M. A. Hanna Co.

**Shipments:**

| | | | |
|---|---|---|---|
| Homer | 1915-1950 | 6,776,617 | Tons |
| Cardiff | 1922-1923 | 144,415 | |
| Homer | 1950-1967 | 8,564,312 | |
| | 1968-1969 | 1,174,824 | |
| | Total | 16,660,168 | Tons |

**Railroad:** C & N W    **Port:** Escanaba, Mich.    **Closed:** 6/27/1969

61

PHOTO ABOVE - CIRCA 1940

**JAMES**

**Location:** Mineral Hills, Iron Co., Mich. N ¹/₂-NE Sec 23 and NW-NW Sec 24 (Spies)-T43N-R35W.
**Description:** Operated since 1906; has shipped every year except 1932. Operated by Mineral Mining Co., prior to acquisition by James Mining Co., January 1, 1925. Once known as Osana. Worked by stoping and sub-level caving method. Depth, 900 ft. Shipments by Mineral Mining Co. during its operation of the James, as shown herein, include tonnages which evidently came from its adjoining Wauseca property in 1911, 1913, 1915-1916, 1918-1920 and 1922.
**Ore:** Soft, yellow, high phosphorus. Some is crushed. Grade shipped. 1950: James.
**Mining Co.:** James Mining Co.     **Agents:** Pickands Mather & Co.     **Closed:** 1953
**Shipments:** 1907-1950  7,684,707 Tons     **Railroad:** C & N W     **Port:** Escanaba, Mich.
　　　　　　 1950-1953    <u>644,891</u>
　　　　　　 Total        8,329,598 Tons

James Mine.    IRON RIVER, Mich.

**Entrance Drifts to James shaft
7th level**

1961

## KIMBALL

**Location:**  Crystal Falls, Iron Co., Mich. E ½ -SE Sec 29-T43N-R32W
**Description:**  Opened 1907; shipped in 1907 and 1915. Mine idle since 1910; last of small accumulated stockpile shipped in 1915. Formerly operated by Corrigan Mc Kinney & Co. Worked by stoping method. Depth, 344 ft.
**Ore:**  Hard, red, high phosphorus. Crushed. Grade shipped, 1915: Kimball.
**Mining Co.:**  Corrigan Mc Kinney & Co. (formerly)
**Shipments:**  1907-1915  35,757 Tons    **Railroad:**  C & N W    **Port:**  Escanaba, Mich.


## LAMONT

**Location:**  Crystal Falls, Iron Co., Mich. Lot 6, in NW-SE Sec 20-T43-R32W
**Description:**  Opened 1889; shipped through 1910, except 1895, 1898, 1901 and 1908-1909. Operated formerly by Corrigan McKinney & Co. Also known as Monitor mine. Lease surrendered October 17, 1910.
**Ore:**  Soft, brown, high phosphorus.    **Mining Co.:**  Corrigan Mc Kinney & Co. (formerly)
**Shipments:**  1889-1910  558, 524 Tons    **Railroad:** C & N W    **Port:**  Escanaba, Mich.

Lamont Engine and Boiler House

## LAWRENCE
*(No Photo Available)*

**Location:** Crystal Falls, Iron Co., Mich. NE-SE Sec 36-T43N-R33W
**Description:** Also known as Wilkinson. A trespass shipment only, made in 1920.
**Mining Co.:** The Verona Mining Co.    **Agent:** Pickands Mather & Co.
**Shipments:** 1920          584 Tons
          1950-1956  6,379
          Total      6963 Tons

## LEE PECK
*(No Photo Available)*

**Location:** Crystal Falls, Iron Co., Mich. SW-NE Sec 26-T43N-R32W
**Shipments:** 1892  2,844 Tons

## LINCOLN
*(No Photo Available)*

**Location:** Crystal Falls, Iron Co., Mich.  W ½- SW Sec 21-T43N-R32W
**Description:** Opened 1891; shipped 1891-1893, 1899-1907 and 1909. Formerly operated by Corrigan Mc Kinney & Co. Originally called Fairbanks. Lease expired November 6, 1917.
**Ore:** High phosphorus.    **Mining Co.:** Corrigan Mc Kinney Steel Co.
**Shipments:** 1891-1909 241,627 Tons    **Railroad:** C & N W and C M St P & P
**Port:** Escanaba, Mich.

## MANSFIELD

**Location:** Crystal Falls, Iron Co., Mich. Lots equivalent to SW-SW Sec 17 and NW-NW Sec 20-T43N-R31W

**Description:** Opened 1890; shipped through 1913, except 1894-1896, 1906 and 1912. Formerly operated by Oliver Iron Mining Co. Depth, 1,517 ft.

**Ore:** Hard, brown, non-bessemer.     **Mining Co.:** Oliver Iron Mining Co.

**Shipments:** 1890-1913  1,462,504 Tons     **Railroad:** C & N W

**Port:** Escanaba, Mich.

## MASTODON
*(See Balkin - Judson)*

**Location:** Alpha, Iron Co., Mich. NE Sec 13-T42N-R33W
**Description:** Opened 1882; shipment in 1942 by Pittsburgh Coke & Iron Co. Originally operated by Mastodon Iron Co. In 1912 leased to Balkan Mining Co. and operated as a part of Balkan-Judson Group of mines. The lease was surrendered at the close of 1935. Worked by sub-level caving. Depth, 484.6 ft.
**Ore:** Soft, red, high phosphorus and manganiferous. Crushed.
**Mining Co.:** The Balkan Mining Co.    **Agent:** Pickands Mather & Co.
**Shipments:** 1882-1896  425,708 Tons
                       1942        21,607
            Total 1882-1942     447,315 (included under Balkan-Judson)
Later shipments included in Balkan, except stockpile shipment in 1942.
**Railroad:** C & N W and C M St P & P    **Port:** Escanaba, Mich.


## SOUTH MASTODON

**Location:** Alpha, Iron Co., Mich. NW-SE Sec 13-T42N-R33W
**Description:** Opened 1887; shipped 1888-1890 when exhausted. Also known as Manhattan.
**Shipments:** 1887-1890  8,203 Tons    **Railroad:** C & N W
**Port:** Escanaba, Mich.


## MC DONALD
*(No Photo Available)*

**Location:** Crystal Falls, Iron Co., Mich. SE-NE Sec 23-T43N-R32W
**Description:** Opened 1908; shipped 1909-1913. Formerly operated by Mc Donald Mining Co. Worked by stoping method.  Depth, 325 ft.
**Ore:** Soft, brown, non-bessemer    **Mining Co.:** Mc Donald Mining Co.
**Agent:** Lake Erie Ore Co.    **Shipments:** 1909-1913  30,289 Tons
**Railroad:** C & N W    **Port:** Escanaba, Mich.


## MICHAELS
*(No Photo Available)*

**Location:** Iron River, Iron Co., Mich. SE Sec 29-T43N-R34W
**Description:** Reserve property. Formerly owned by Corrigan Mc Kinney Steel Co. Acquired by Republic Steel Corp. in 1935.    **Interests:** Republic Steel Corp.

**MICHIGAN**

**Location:** Amasa, Iron Co., Mich. NE-NW Sec 9-T44N-R33W
**Description:** Opened 1893; shipped 1893-1895, 1897, 1902, 1905-1908, 1910 and 1913-1916. Formerly operated by Oliver Iron mining Co. Originally called the Gibson. Depth, 656 ft. Leased in 1948 by North Range Mining Co. and now included in Warner mine.
**Ore:** Hard, brown, high phosphorus. Part shipped as lump.    **Mining Co.:** North Range Mining Co.
**Shipments:** 1893-1916  350,270 Tons    **Railroad:** C & N W
**Port:** Escanaba, Mich.

**NEELY**
*(No Photo Available)*

**Location:** Crystal Falls, Iron Co., Mich. Lots 1 and 2, E ½ -SW Sec 21-T43N-R32W
**Description:** A reserve property, under lease by Inland Steel Co. since July 1948.
**Interests:** Inland Steel Co.

## MONONGAHELA

**Location:** Crystal Falls, Iron Co., Mich. NE-NW, N ½ -NE and SE-NE Sec 36-T43N-R33W
**Description:** Opened 1901; shopped 1901 and 1903. Reopened in 1915 and shipped 1916, 1918-1927, 1931 and 1933-1934. Formerly operated by Hanna Furnace Co. (Hollister Mining Co) later by Hanna Iron Ore Co. Shipment from trespass by Columbia mine in 1943. Acquired by Republic Steel Corp. in 1951; being developed for operation with Columbia.
**Ore:** Hard and soft, red, high phosphorus. Grade shipped, 1934: Monongahela.
**Mining Co.:** Republic Steel Corp.     **Shipments:** 1901-1943  1,352,591 Tons
**Railroad:** C & N W and C M St P & P     **Port:** Escanaba, Mich.

## NANAIMO
*(No Photo Available)*

**Location:** Iron River, Iron Co., Mich. W ½ -SW Sec 26-T43N-R35W
**Description:** Opened 1882; shipped 1882-1884, 1886-1888, 1890-1891 and 1904-1908. Operated initially by Nanaimo Mining Co.; later by Mineral Mining Co. Worked by sub-level caving method. Depth, 362 ft. Beta, NE-SW Sec 26, once included in this property, but its shipments are shown separately.
**Ore:** Soft, yellow, high phosphorus.
**Mining Co.:** Mineral Mining Co.     **Shipments:** 1882-1908  373,765 Tons.
**Railroad:** C & N W and C M St P & P     **Port:** Escanaba, Mich.

71

**ODGERS**

**Location:** Crystal Falls, Iron Co., Mich. S ½ -NE Sec 30T43N-R32W
**Description:** Opened 1916; shipped every year through 1935, except 1931. Operated by Corrigan Mc Kinney Steel Co. which merged with Republic Steel Corp. in 1935. Republic surrendered lease in 1936. Worked by stoping method. Depth, 868 ft.
**Ore:** Soft, reddish-brown, high phosphorus. Crushed. Grade shipped, 1935, Odgers.
**Mining Co.:** Republic Steel Corp.     **Shipments:** 1916-1935  2,101,381 Tons
**Railroad:**  C & N W and C M St P & P     **Port:** Escanaba, Mich.

## PAINT RIVER
*(No Photo Available)*

**Location:** Crystal Falls, Iron Co., Mich. NE-SE and Lots 4 and 5 Sec 20-T43N-R32W

**Description:** Formerly known as Fairbanks, which opened 1882 and shipped through 1913, except 1893-1898, 1901,and 1908-1912. Operated by Corrigan McKinney Steel Co. before merger with Republic Steel Corp. in 1935.

**Ore:** Soft, red, high phosphorus.    **Interests:** Republic Steel Corp

**Shipments:** 1882-1913  382,078 Tons    **Railroad:** C & N W    **Port:** Escanaba, Mich.


## PERRY
*(No Photo Available)*

**Location:** Unknown. No record except of shipment.

**Shipment:** 1883    3,138 Tons


## PORTER
*(No Photo Available)*

**Location:**  Amasa, Iron Co., Mich. N ½ -NE and SE-NE Sec 22-T44N-R33W

**Description:** Also called Amasa Porter. Opened 1914; shipped every year through 1927. Mine first operated by the Nevada Mining Co. (Oglebay, Norton & Co., Agent), and later by Hemlock River Mining Co. (Pickands Mather & Co., Agent) Worked by sub-level caving method. Depth, 850 ft. A reserve property of Inland Steel Co.

**Ore:** Soft, red,non-bessemer. Partly crushed. Grade shipped, 1927:Cedar.

**Interests:** Inland Steel Co.    **Shipments:** 1916-1927  733,327 Tons.

**Railroad:** C M St P & P    **Port:** Escanaba, Mich.


## RAVENNA-PRICKETT
*(No Photo Available)*

**Location:** Crystal Falls, Iron Co., Mich.  Ravenna, S ½ -N ½ , SW and W ½ -SE Sec 19-T43N-R32W; Prickett, NE-SW, N1.2 –SE and SE-NE Sec 24-T43N-R33W.

**Description:** Ravenna opened 1911. Shipped every year through 1917. Formerly operated by Hollister Mining Co.; later by Hanna Iron Ore Co. ( The M. A. Hanna Co., Agent). Reopened by Inland Steel Co. with adjacent Prickett property. Shipped 1940-1943. Ravenna mine was worked by stoping. Inland operated as open pit, then under-ground. Leases surrendered 1943.

**Ore:** Hard and soft, red, high phosphorus. Grades shipped, 1943: Ravenna and Prickett.

**Mining Co.:** Inland Steel Co.    **Shipments:** 1911-1943  635,227 Tons

**Railroad:** C & N W and C M St P & P    **Port:** Escanaba, Mich.

## RICHARDS (Dunn)

**Location:** Crystal Falls, Iron Co., Mich. S ½-SE Sec 36-T43N-R33W
**Description:** Opened 1913; shipped 1913-1921, 1923 and 1926-1927. Operated by Corrigan McKinney
Steel Co. Lease surrendered August 14, 1927. **Ore:** Soft, brown, high phosphorus
**Mining Co.:** Corrigan McKinney Steel Co. (formerly) **Shipments:** 1913-1927 -- 534,448 Tons
**Railroad:** C & N W **Port:** Escanaba, Mich.

74

## RIVERTON GROUP

**Location:** Iron River, Iron Co, Mich. Riverton, E ¹/₂ -NE Sec 35 and (Iron River) NW-NW Sec 36-T43N-R35W; Dober, NW Sec 1; Duff, E ¹/₂-NE Sec 2-T42N-R35W; Isabella, SW-SW Sec 36-T43N-R35W. Dober, Duff and Isabella are now part of Hiawatha No 2.
**Description:** Opened 1882; shipped every year through 1937, except 1893-1897 and 1932-1934. Shipments in 1935-1937 were from stockpile. Operated by Oliver Iron Mining Co. Depth, 1,750. Leases on Dober, Duff and Isabella surrendered in 1933, and new leases taken by The M. A. Hanna Co. to form Hiawatha No. 2 mine, which has shipped since 1935.   **Ore:** Soft, brown, high phosphorus and manganiferous. Grade shipped, 1937: Barton.   **Mining Co:** Oliver Iron Mining Co.
**Shipments:** 1882-1937 5,881,550 Tons   **Railroads:** C & N W   **Port:** Escanaba, Mi.

*Open Pit at Riverton Mine -- Stambaugh, Michigan.*

*Riverton Mine*

**ROGERS**

**Location:** Iron River, Iron Co., Mich. SW Sec 21 and W ° and NE Sec 29-T43N-R34W. Includes Blair, SW Sec 29; Erickson, SW Sec 21; Swanson, S ¹/₂ - NE Sec. 29; Schiebler, NE-NE Sec 29; Paulsen, NW-NE Sec 29 and White, E ¹/₂ -NW Sec 29.

**Description:** Opened 1912; shipped every year through 1945, except 1921, 1934,1938-1939 and 1943-1944. Shipments from stockpile 1937-1945 included. Formerly operated by Munro Iron Mining Co., now by Hanna Iron Ore Co. (The M. A. Hanna Co., Agent). Worked by caving method. Depth, 500 ft. The Blair-Erickson are underground explorations not yet opened.

**Ore:** Hard, red, high phosphorus and manganiferous. Crushed. Constituent of grade shipped, 1945: Weir.

**Mining Co.:** The M. A. Hanna Co.     **Shipments:** 1914-1945  2,907,375 Tons.     **Railroad:** C & N W

**Port:** Escanaba, Mich.

**SHERIDAN**

**Location:** Iron River, Iron Co., Mich. SE-SE Sec 26-T43N-R35W

**Description:** Opened 1889; shipped every year until exhausted in 1900, except 1894 and 1898.

**Mining Co.:** Pickands Mather & Co.     **Shipments:** 1889-1900  116,299 Tons     **Railroad:** C & N W

**Port:** Escanaba, Mich.

## SPIES-VIRGIL

**Location:** Iron River, Iron Co., Mich. Spies, E ½ -NW; and Virgil, SW-NW Sec 24-T43N-R35W
**Description:** Spies opened 1916 and shipped through 1927. Inactive until 1945 when it began shipping and has shipped each year, 1945-1950. Closed 1955.
Virgil opened 1912 and shipped 1912-1914, 1916, 1918 and 1925-1946 except 1934. Worked by sublevel stoping method. Depth, 1,256 ft.
**Ore:** Soft, red, high phosphorus. Crushed. Constituent of grade shipped, 1950: Virgil.
**Mining Co.:** The Cleveland-Cliffs Iron Co.    **Railroad:** C & N W    **Port:** Escanaba, Mich.
**Shipments:** Spies   1917-1950   1,234,504 Tons
                1950-1956    911,461
      Virgil   1912-1946   <u>2,049,146</u>
               Total    4,195,111 Tons

Sherwood Mine

## CAMPBELL-SHERWOOD
*(No Photo Available)*

**Location:** Iron River, Iron Co., Mich. NW Sec 26-T43N-R34W
**Description:** A reserve property. No shipments.    **Interests:** Inland Steel Co.

# SHERWOOD
*(See Photo On Previous Page)*

**Location:** Iron River, Iron Co., Mich. SE-NE, NE-SE Sec 23-T43N-R35W
**Description:** Opened 1931 by Republic Steel Corp. and shipped 1931,1933 and 1936. Ore was taken out through Spies-Virgil mine. Acquired by Inland Steel Co. in 1943 and has shipped each year, 1943-1950. Worked by sub-level stoping.
**Ore:** Semi-hard, reddish-brown, high phosphorus. Crushed.
 **Mining Co.:** Inland Steel Co.
**Shipments:** 1931 -1950   2,880,816     **Railroad**: C & N W     **Port**: Escanaba, Mich.
               1950-1967   7,026,967
               1968-1969     739,850
               1970-1975   2,204,855
               1976-1978     860,579
               Total          13,713,067

# TOBIN

**Location:** Crystal Falls, Iron Co., Mich. SW Sec 30-T43N-R32W
**Description:** Opened 1901; shipped every year through 1950, except 1921, 1926, 1929, 1931 and 1943-1948. Shipments 1938-1940 from stockpile. Operated by Corrigan, McKinney Steel Col; acquired by Republic Steel Corp in 1935. Worked by sub-level stoping method. Depth, 1,783 ft. Worked in conjunction with Columbia mine.
**Ore:** Semi-hard, reddish-brown, high phosphorus. Crushed. Grade shipped, 1950: Tobin-Columbia.
**Mining Co.:** Republic Steel Corp.
**Shipments:** 1901-1950   4,630,052 Tons
               1950-1962   2,033,642
               Total          6,663,694 Tons
**Railroad**: C & NW     **Port**: Escanaba, Mich.

**WARNER**

**Location:** Amasa, Iron Co., Mich. E ½ -NW, SW-NE, NE-SW and SE Sec 9; SW-SW Sec 10; E ½ NW and NE-NW Sec 15; and NE-NE Sec 16-T44N-R33E. Includes Michigan, NE-NW Sec 9; Gibson, NW-NW Sec 15; former Warner which included SE Sec 9; and Bay Shore, NE-NE Sec 16.

**Description:** The former Warner as above described was opened in 1915; shipped every year through 1934 except 1932. Operated by Hemlock River Mining Co. (Pickands Mather & Co., Agent) . Lease surrendered to fee owners in 1934. Worked by stoping method. Depth, 1,239 ft., 11th level. Small stock-pile clean-up shipment made in 1937 by L. E Ives, Inc. The former Warner together with the Michigan and Gibson and adjacent tracts, were leased by North Range Mining Co. in 1948. Mine pumped out and explored 1949-1950. Equipped for production, 1950. First shipments, 1951.

**Ore:** Hard, red and purple non-bessemer. Grade shipped, 1934: Cedar.

**Mining Co.:** North Range Mining Co.

**Shipments:**

| | | |
|---|---|---|
| 1915-1937 | 1,868,637 | Tons |
| 1951-1957 | 966,290 | |
| Total | 2,834,927 | Tons |

**Railroad:** C & N W    **Port:** Escanaba, Mich.

## WAUSECA-ARONSON

**Location:** Iron River, Iron Co., Mich. SE-NW and SW-NE (Wauseca); E ½ -NW-SE (Aronson) Sec 23-T43N-R35W

**Description:** Wauseca opened 1926; shipped through 1929. Operated by Mineral Mining Co. Sometimes known as Konwinski. Stockpile shipments in 1940 and 1941 made by The M. A. Hanna Co. Assigned to Hanna Coal & Ore Corp. in 1941, with the Aronson, and has shipped each year 1942 to closing 6/27/1969. Sub-level stoping. Depth, 1,142 ft. Shipments from Aronson started in 1947 and continued to closing. Shipments sometimes reported as from the Wauseca in 1911, 1913, 1915, 1916, 1918-1920, and 1922, evidently were made by the James ( or Osana) mine, and are credited thereto in this volume.

**Ore:** Hard, red,high phorsphorus. Crushed, part screened. Grade shipped, 1950: Wauseca

**Mining Co.:** Hanna Coal & Ore Corp.     **Agent:** The M. A. Hanna Co.

**Shipments:** Wauseca 1926-1950    3,066,704 Tons
          Aronson  1947-1950       704,975
      Production       1950-1967  10,484,639
                   1968         <u>567,508</u>
                 Total     14,822,826 Tons

**Railroad:** C & N W     **Port:** Escanaba, Mich.

## WICKWIRE

**Location:** Iron River, Iron Co., Mich. NE-NW and NW-NE Sec 35-T42N-R35W. NW-NE Sec 35 is now included in Hiawatha No. 1.

**Description:** Opened 1911; shipped through 1917, except 1915. Worked by slicing and caving methods. Depth, 313 ft. Production section now a part of Hiawatha No. 1, operated by Hanna Iron Ore. Co.

**Ore:** Medium, red-brown, high phosphorus.     **Mining Co.:** Wickwire Mining Co.

**Agent:** Wickwire Steel Co.     **Shipments:** 1911-1917 128,869 Tons

**Railroad:** C & N W     **Port:** Escanaba, Mich.

## YOUNGS

**Location:** Gaastra, Iron Co., Mich. E $\frac{1}{2}$ -E $\frac{1}{2}$ Sec 12-T42N-R35W
**Description:** Opened 1905; shipped 1905-1913, 1916-1918, 1920, 1927 and 1928. Prior to 1914 operated by Huron Iron Mining Co. (Lake Erie Ore Co., Agent). G. W. Youngs Mining Co. was the operator, 1914-1919; The Florence Iron Co., 1920-1923; and Newman Ore Co. (Marquette Ore Co., Agent), 1923-1929. Also known as Newman. Worked by back and sub-stoping. Depth, 518 ft.
**Ore:** Hard, brown, high phosphorus. Shipped as Youngs grade prior to 1927 and as Newman grade in 1927 and 1928.   **Mining Co.:** Newman Ore Co. (formerly)
**Agent:** Marquette Ore Co. (formerly)   **Shipments:** 1905-1928   802,751 Tons
**Railroad:** C & N W   **Port:** Escanaba, Mich.

## YOUNGSTOWN

**Location:** Crystal Falls, Iron Co., Mich. W $\frac{1}{2}$ -SW Sec 20-T43N-R32W
**Description:** Opened 1882; shipped 1882-1884, 1886-1888, 1890-1891, 1895 and 1897. Formerly an Oliver Iron Mining Co. operation for the Illinois Steel Co. From 1926-1931 the NW-SW Sec 20 was operated by Oglebay, Norton & Co. for the Bristol Mining Co., under agreement with the Oliver Iron Mining Co., as a part of the Bristol-Youngstown. Leased by Inland Steel Co., 1949, reopened together with the Bristol as Bristol-Youngstown with shipment in 1950.
**Mining Co:** Inland Steel Co.   **Shipments:** 1882-1897   151,425 Tons
**Railroad:** C & N W and C M St P & P   **Port:** Escanaba, Mich.

Mine rescue team about 1920.
Sometimes (poisonous) sulphur gas was found in the tunnels.

# MINING INSPECTION- *1980-2001, Peter Korach*

I was born in Crosby, Minnesota, and my dad was a miner for forty years. Most of the mining there was underground. I worked sixteen years for Inland Steel in Crosby and then I got transferred here to the Sherwood Mine in 1966 and I worked 11 years. When the mine shut, I went into a different profession.

I was a miner when I first came here, but we did a different type of mining in Minnesota so Mr. Edwards, our Superintendent here, and our captain kept most of us guys (from Minnesota) working with each other because we worked the straight raises and stuff there where the miners here did not. We used more tuggers than they did to haul our supplies up. We never carried them like the miners from Michigan did…When they moved up one sub, they had to take all their rods and their machines and pull them up with a rope. We just put them in the bucket and raised them up.

And what we did, they didn't have any air tuggers here so me and Henry Ravnick we went out and seen our superintendent over there. They had already thrown these tuggers out in the junk pile and we asked him if we could have them to take back to Michigan. He told us to take all of them. They weren't very big. They had a three inch cable on them. You'd put them on a pole and you could lift or tug anything with it. This is what we had. In my place we had three of them…one on top and two on the bottom. You had one on the middle sub too. Your middle sub was what was called the scraping sub. Say we had to hoist a scraper blade, the guys from Michigan would pull it up by hand. We just hooked on that cable and pulled it up. Me and my partner could move our tools in half an hour. All our rods, hoses, two or three different machines— these machines weighed 70, 80, 90 pounds, you know.

When I worked contract, there was something called Company Count. At the Sherwood Mine there was three and one-half cars per man—these little cars that you had underground. That's what they called company count, so anything over that you got a bonus. You could never get paid for less than the three and one-half cars per day. If you made extra, it would be divided four ways between you and your three other partners, the same as the powder. They allowed you so much cost to break a ton of dirt. As soon as you went over that contract you split with the other three guys and the company kept half. It would be an incentive for you to try to have more production.

Everyday they checked you. They knew how much powder you used because you had to get your powder out of the powder house. They charged everything to your contract—your axes, etc. were charged to your contract as a certain number of dollars. All your mining gear like your boots, your rain gear, you got cheaper. I think it was $2.00 for a suit, gloves 80 cents. They knew how much you took out of your place— 50 cars, 70 cars, they knew how much you got everyday—that goes into the office and the two guys up in the office who figure out what your contract is.

If you were developing, then you were measured by the foot. If you were mining, where you were getting dirt, then you went by the car. You had to get three and one-half cars done per man—you started bonus after that. If you didn't get three and one-half cars…say you had a tough place you still got your Company Count. So, me and my partner would have to get seven cars a day and the other two partners same thing so that was fourteen. But say you got seventy-five cars that day. That was bonus. We tripled our base now and then.

We got lots of water. See you always had water until you hit the ore body and when you were on the bottom the water would just dry right up. And the water would follow you. We ditched and the water went into the sump pump and the sump pump took care of it. They had big pumps in the Sherwood Mine. I think they were something like 2000 gallons a minute. Two big stainless steel pumps—one would run for so many minutes on the hour and then the other one would kick in so many minutes on the hour.

Underground we were all belts. The Homer had a few belts. They had the cars deep in the mine then they'd come out and they'd put it into the pocket and the belt would take the ore to the shaft. They could shut them off. The guy at the shaft had lights so he could tell as soon as our raises were filled with dirt we had a light off so they would know down at the shop that our raises were full so they would start the belt. The belt dumped into another pocket down at the shaft—probably held 40-50 cars—two big pockets. Then the skips would come down and the skip tender would load it—so much goes into the skip pocket, that goes into the skip, then the skip goes and the other one comes down.

At the Sherwood, we were at the 1900 foot level as we had put in a decline at the 1650 level. The ore from there came up on a belt up to the 1900 and then it went onto another belt that took it to the shaft. They made a lot per man.

Now that I'm Mine Inspector, I don't know where all the stopes were, but I knew where 90 % of the properties were, but I've got 135 parcels that had some kind of either exploration going on or mining. Some of them are just an old remnant of a fence, probably a little depression and stuff like that. As for filling up their stopes before they left, Hanna and Inland did some but never completely. If you read the book that Dr. Johnson (Houghton Tech.) wrote, he and McDonald in 1976-77 that had that first analysis of the mines, there's eleven critical areas on the West side and six or seven critical areas on the East side that could result in loss of property and/or lives…On this side I would say the bad place is where we had the (recent) cave, then M-189 and the Delta underneath that park there. I was against that and I didn't think the state should get involved in giving money to the city for that. When men like Mr. Johnson and McDonald did the survey and said that there was a possibility of a loss of property and/or life, I think we'd better heed that stuff. I don't remember when they were bumping the ore cars across U.S. 2 at East Genesee and not sending the engine over or when they kept pumping stuff into that bridge in the spring.

## Subsidence, April 2001

It was the Old Baltic Mine #1 shaft. It's just a little bit north of the road there. The road goes out by the old Knights of Columbus Hall probably about 150 feet in. It was a shaft (not a stope). When Gaastra put their sewer line in it probably wasn't caved in that far so that they engineered their sewer line to go through there. So now when the shaft caved, it was found to be only 3 or 4 feet from the sewer line. I look for it to go down again but I mean it's hard for me to say that it will, but I just feel that something's going to go down there again cause you have the water on one side and I don't know, I just don't like it. What we did there now is fill it as much as we could and we're going to look for different funding.

Last year we had a major subsidence over at Amasa—the old Hemlock Mine. I got a telephone call from a guy that a kid was riding his four wheeler and saw it and it was a big subsidence. It was about a third the size of this room (30'x 50') and I don't know how deep. I threw a fishing rod down in there but I couldn't find the bottom—it seemed like I hit water. Then I got the prisoners out there and they put fencing around the area. No filling was done as it would be pretty hard.

I check most of the mines twice a year. A lot of them are the same as they were when I first started. If the mining companies still have the property, I don't have any problems. All I have to do is call them, and they'll set up the work order and they'll fix it. The Attorney General's ruling is it is the mineral rights owner that's responsible. If you owned the surface and the mineral rights then you would be liable.

I'm bonded—I had a hundred counts against me where that boy was killed and that was one of the better fences that I had. That went on for three or four years. They finally settled. I don't know what the settlement ever was, but they got Stambaugh for public nuisance. I don't know if there was a fine or not. All I know is that a twenty-one year old kid climbed the fence with his brother and this other kid went down that hole. I had signs there and it was one of the better fences I had…I knew they couldn't do anything to me because of that $1,000,000 bonding.

I'd like to hire someone to train to take my place and teach them by showing them instead of how I had to learn from the books. It's a lot easier that way. I'm not going to run again because I'm seventy years old.

H.B.  4/29/2001

# OVERVIEW OF UNIONISM DEVELOMENT IN IRON COUNTY
## *Marcia Bernhardt*

In the early 19th century, the legal relationship of employer and employee was still that of master and servant, a relic of the feudal system. Prior to that time, the first recorded strike in America took place in 1741 when New York bakers quit work as a protest against an ordinance regulating the price of bread.

A successful attempt to establish a 10-hour day was made in Philadelphia in 1835. However, in 1842 the Supreme Judicial Court of Massachusetts ruled that employees might lawfully organize for mutual aid.

Two unions emerged on a national scale in the 1870's—the National Labor Union and the Noble Order of the Knights of Labor. The present American Federation of Labor claims continuity of existence through its records from 1881. The IWW or "Wobblies" (International Workers of the World) was a militant organization founded in Chicago in 1905 by William (Big Bill) Haywood, the radical secretary-treasurer of the Western Federation of Mines, with the aid of American Socialist leaders, Daniel De Leon and Eugene Debs.

## The Early Movement in Iron County

A dated photograph (1912) of the Workers' Hall in Crystal Falls, part of the Iron County Museum photo collection, indicates that the IWW, International Workers of the World, organized in Iron County. The Iron River Workers' Hall, which still stands, the second dwelling on the left as one ascends Stambaugh Hill from U.S. 2, was probably built about the same time.

In 1974 an oral history interview on Finnish Socialist Activity recounted some early aspects of the labor movement locally. The interviewee first carefully defined the difference in Socialism—the anti-IWW Socialists and the so called, "Yellow Socialists". In the third and fourth decades of this century, several local families among these "Yellow Socialist" converts to communism went to Karelia, Russia, believing they would find an ideal society there.

The interviewee went on to describe the IWW union organization locally as taking place in about 1917. His father served as an agent and if somebody needed dues stamps to fill their cards, they could buy them from him. It was also during this period that heavy organizing was going on in Bisbee, Arizona, in the copper mines. "Being a small town, they knew, they had easy ways of knowing who the organizer was, and he (Dad) had to start making tracks from Iron River…He had them (stamps) buried in the basement. There was only one room in the basement and there was a trapdoor and there was dirt there…he (buried) them in a pail…The pamphlets were hidden in the hollow center leg of the dining room table. These were the small propaganda pamphlets…he built a dummy bottom so he could just turn it and the bottom stayed in there and the propaganda would be sitting (there)."

To further describe the "house cleaning" time, which took place in April 1919, Federal agents in their search found an "Industrial" share from the Industrialist paper and an IWW songbook in the home. To quote the investigator, "I see you've been buying Liberty Bonds."—a pun on workers' freedom. The investigators also appropriated the book <u>Industrial Civilization</u> written by Leo Laukki, who along with Big Bill Haywood sought refuge in Russia.

As a result of the raid and union activity here, the interviewee's father, who was working for Barnie Krom of Krom's Department Store in Iron River at the time, was fired because of his union known affiliation. In retaliation, Barnie lost a lot of business as the Finns all boycotted the store.

In concluding his recollections, the interviewee, who is of Finnish descent, commented, "Somehow or other in the northern areas of Wisconsin, Minnesota and Michigan, the Finns were very heavy in the IWW movement. It was an offshoot of the socialists, (there) wasn't very many of them…The government broke the back of the IWW. They accused them of aiding and abetting and inciting people not to register for the draft. (We left the area) but the IWW as far as I know stayed active after 1923 even…perhaps it petered out in the early Thirties, during the Depression."

## The Movement Grows

The decade of the 30's brought big changes to Iron County. Among them were the reduction in the number of mines and also a decrease in production. In 1930 there were 28 producing mines—one of the most productive years in the century of operation. Reports show production at 3,800,098 tons with 2,265 men employed. Ten years later in 1940, only 10 mines were in operation and production was 1,481,331 tons by 1,167 workers.

The Iron County Labor movement that found earlier roots with the Industrial Workers of the World began to organize. In April 1934, twenty miners met to sign up with the A. F. of L. (American Federation of Labor) at the Eagles Hall in Iron River. According to the *Reporter* editorial, "Representatives of the National Miners' Union protested charges that their organization was Communistic, but openly avowed personal sympathies for a radical party, which almost brought the meeting to an end…"The organizer, George Cole of Salt Lake City, Utah had come here after the local committee from the Bates Mine asked for information.

A subsequent report notes that sixty members joined at a meeting at the Caspian City Hall. Officers elected were Placido Lauent, president; Earl Clark, secretary; Max Margoni, treasurer; and Valentine Frizzo, Celeste Comforti, Celeste Casari and Archili Zanbiase, members of the executive committee.

A second editorial in the *Iron River Reporter* in the following October expressed sympathy for the more conservative A.F. of L. "Iron County has been the spearhead of a movement in the Upper Peninsula to organize workers of all classes. The A.F. of L. has had a paid organizer in the district for many months, and he has been active among the mining employees. Somewhat out of step as to methods, but sympathetic as to objectives has been a Communist group of leaders who have marshaled into local union groups, known as the Iron County Labor Union, many not affiliated with the mines.." The editorial continued with the warning against the more militant National Mine Workers"…If the Union group persist in naming leaders who find greater satisfaction in creating disturbances than they do in securing benefits, their usefulness and standing will be seriously impaired."

Interviews with Fino Sartorelli and Ernest Gordon, early local union leaders, concur that the Mine, Mill, and Smelter Workers came to organize in 1934. A strike had been set for November 1 at Hiawatha no. 1 and no. 2. "They wanted to get fans in there to get fresh air into the working places. The company wouldn't do it, so they wanted to go on strike." Organizers from Denver headquarters informed the local that the union was not yet recognized, so strike plans were dropped.

In April, 1935, employees asked for recognition of the International Union of Mine, Mill and Smelter Workers at the Davidson. In May there were strike rumblings across the peninsula and Upper Wisconsin. Demands were: reduction of the working day from 8 to 7 hours, a 50% increase in hourly wage paid mine workers—now $4.40 per day or 55 cents an hour to a new rate of $5.77, seniority rights at each local mine, abolition of contract labor and assigning a pumpman's helper when the mine was not running. William Suksi, Secretary of the Upper Michigan Miners' Executive Board indicated the principal question in regard to the proposed strike was the right of the unemployed miner to vote.

An editorial in April stated, " (While) sympathy for the 'forgotten man' having been nursed by five years of depression, two basic disputes must be removed before adequate collective bargaining can be achieved—the company union and the corollary question of the right of a majority to speak for all employees…"

Shortly thereafter, Union leaders announced a strike call for the following week. Voting showed Iron River local 65 %, less than required; Gaastra, 95% in favor, Crystal Falls, 82% in favor. Ironwood and Bessemer locals were almost unanimous, while Wakefield and Ramsey were 87% favorable. Mine officials that few favored a walkout. Union officials accused mine officials of coercive and intimidating tactics. Another editorial claimed that more accurate information was available—that "working miners to the extent of 85-90% were content to work under present conditions." The union, on the other hand, indicated that picket lines would be formed. However, the strike date passed with no action.

Sartorelli and Gordon continued in their interview, "We were without a union until the spring of 1937. Then twelve or fourteen of us signed a letter to get the organizers here. The biggest problem here was breaking up the company unions…They (workers) had to vote if they wanted to belong to the company union or the CIO. At that time, they beat us in the election, but it only lasted about a year….they were afraid to vote the CIO that time as they were afraid they were going to be laid off and lose their jobs. But it worked the opposite. The ones that were CIO stayed on the job and the ones that had more rights were laid off. That was in 1938. In 1939 the mines were slacking off, just before the war broke out."

In looking back at the decade of the 30's one must credit action from the national scene. The National Labor Relations Act, better known as the Wagner Act after the chief sponsor, Senator Robert F. Wagner of New York, was passed July 5, 1935. The act set up an independent board which was authorized to investigate complaints, issue cease and desist orders against unfair practices in labor relations affecting interstate commerce, safeguard the right to bargain collectively and arbitrate labor disputes. While the act was to bring phenomenal success in the peaceful settlement of disputes, it was under continuous fire both from employers and from the A.F. of L. which charged discrimination in favor of the rival C.I.O. It was not until 1937 that the act was fully implemented.

Early victories recorded report steel corporations raised wages and slashed weekly work hours in March 1937. A 10 cent an hour increase from 52 $\frac{1}{2}$ to 62 $\frac{1}{2}$ cents was announced by Inland Steel Pickands Mather. Hanna established a basic wage rate of $5 a day, time and a half for overtime and a 40 hour week.

**Action Increases**

In June 1937 a meeting was held at the Iron River City Hall to organize a Mine Workers Union with representatives from the Bates, Homer, Hiawatha No. 1 and Hiawatha No. 2 mines. The organization was seen as an effort to offset gains reported by the CIO. Such a local union was to make CIO appeals ineffectual in the county and organizers claimed to have 55 percent sign-up at Hanna mines.

In August three speakers assailed company union. Henry Burkhammer, Steel Workers Organizing Committee organizer of Duluth, was quoted as saying, "Are there Communists among CIO ranks?…probably there are, but I would prefer a communist CIO member to a scab who bucks the movement's progress."

Sartorelli and Gordon again recorded their recollections of the situation, "We were collecting dues and even after we won, people were still afraid. They'd come and pay their dues, a dollar a month then, and they'd watch to see that there were no shift bosses or captains looking for them. They'd sneak. A lot of the time we couldn't even see who paid, we had to guess. A few months we'd have a lot of union members, and three or four months go by, we'd lose them all. We'd have to go back out again, go house to house and hold a meeting to get them back again, until we won the rights to the check-off system in the mine. Then we didn't have to worry."

The check-off system permitted members to sign union cards and the company had insurance cards, which the miners also signed. The ones who could not sign, put an X. The workers at the Spies Mine were the first to win an election.

**Special Cases**

In a "watershed" case the National Labor Relations Board found Hanna Company guilty of unfair labor practices under the Wagner Act. In January 1938 Henry Frostell filed a case against the company when it refused to reinstate him "for reasons that said Henry Frostell had been an admitted member in the International Union of Mines, Mill, and Smelter Workers, Local 125, and that he desired to be represented through a union in negotiations with the company." The claim was that "There is no rule followed by mining companies in recalling men to work except to honor seniority and competency and family needs…No election has been held in the county to determine bargaining representatives for its men through three unions, the Independent, and CIO and AF of L affiliates."

Testimony at the National Labor Relations Board included statements from William Koponen who said that he quit the CIO because he was afraid membership would affect his job. John Dallafior testified that his boss had called the union "a bunch of reds." An Eagloski declared members of Mine Workers' union and some non-union working at similar work were paid 75 cents more per foot in contract than CIO miners on two levels. An attorney for the company asked that these statements be stricken from the record. At the conclusion in October 1938, the Hanna Company lost its appeal.

In 1939 employees at Hanna mines received a five-day week and a 25 percent boost in pay. At the same time, an agreement was reached with the Verona Company by the CIO. In June 1940 it marked an increased heightening of union organization. Workers at the James, Buck, and Bengal (Pickands-Mather Mines) formed an independent union with approximately 65 men. Walter Smethurs, executive secretary to John L. Lewis, addressed the 12th Congressional Conference held in Caspian on Social legislation sponsored by CIO mining unions and timber workers' union. Items in the Wage and Hour Act were reviewed—30 cents per hour minimum and time and a half for overtime if worked in excess of 42 hours.

In September the CIO asked the National Labor Relations Board not to certify Independent Mine Employees as collective bargaining representatives, charging the companies guilty of unfair labor practices similar to those charged M.A. Hanna in 1938. They again accused the company of coercion, intimidation and dominating the labor organization. Charges were brought by the CIO affiliate, Local 1624.

Local mines that supported the CIO effectively used the NLRB (National Labor Relations Board) to back their efforts to organize the local miners and fight off company unions. By 1924 when production climbed for the war effort, all local mines were represented by United Steel Workers of America.

**Unions in the Forties**

In 1924 the Spies Local 2533 was organized with former members of Local 1624. At the Davidson, miners claimed an extra hour pay for riding the cage in a grievance case in February, this to compensate for the time going up and down the shaft. In the following July, the CIO accepted the company offer on overtime in "collar-to-collar" cases. Labor unrest continued with the revelation that war profiteering was going on. On the other side of the coin, mine owners were protesting new tax figures as excessive and threatened to close until after the war was over.

By 1924 when 16 mines were operating, iron miners received the highest annual wage yet—$1,886. To contrast, in 1933, 15 mines were operating and the average wage was $365 per year. However, in November when the CIO and Hanna Company began to talk contract, there were three issues set aside for submission to the War Labor Board—a 44 cent a day wage increase, the check-off, the maintenance of membership clauses, and a collection of other lesser points. My March 1943, the WLB listed terms of agreement which gave the requested wage increase, directed the companies to collect $1.00 monthly union dues and remit to the International, collect as well the $3.00 initial fee, and banned coercion by the company.

A new grievance was brought up in February 1944. Sherwood Local 2709, supported by Hanna Local 1624, made a 100 percent protest against the practice of employing one man on a machine "which cost the life of one of our brothers."

In January 1945, Pickands-Mather and Hanna mines went back to a 6 day week. "Due to emergency demands for increased supplies of war material of all kinds, it is desirable to increase our production…" Shortly after, all mines in Iron County were on a 6 day week and double shifts. In August it was announced that miners would, because of their heavy work, be eligible for more rations.

As the country shifted from wartime to peacetime economy, negotiations between companies and unions changed. In February 1946 to support a national strike by the Steel Workers' Union, local union miners quit jobs peaceably and pickets guarded mine gates, often on lonely vigils in sub-zero weather. A strikers' parade through Caspian, Stambaugh, and Iron River was organized. Taverns adopted a 6 p.m. closing time during the strike and 17 taverns and vending places suspended sales of alcoholic beverages. Issues at stake were miners felt they should be paid for the lunch hour as lunch rooms were very uncomfortable underground, or they should be brought up at noon for health sake, pay should be portal to portal, and travel time should be given for landers. Miners were also holding out for an 18 $\frac{1}{2}$ cent per hour raise. The companies agreed to the hourly raise after 105 days, and mines resumed operations toward the end of April and 12 ore trains were dispatched to waiting ore boats.

In February 1947, CIO locals filed portal pay suits against all companies. A total of 4,721 persons from 26 Michigan concerns were asking for a settlement of $33,629,200. Locally, negotiations with Hanna for a 10 cent an hour wage increase were expected in April. The Pickands-Mather Union avoided a strike by signing 20 minutes before the deadline for 12 $\frac{1}{2}$ cents per hour.

While during the 40's, companies instituted safety programs and prizes were given for perfect records as a part of mandated betterment of working condition, unions themselves were activating programs and projects of their own as they became more politically involved.

In early 1949 at a meeting in Caspian, 75 people representing all unions, attended to discuss the formation of credit unions, collective bargaining and political action. Suggested plans were actuated and in June, presidents of each local were asked to send three delegates each to a meeting, in the Iron River Warshawsky building.

A strike called in September ended in November after 44 days and 1,700 miners returned to their jobs. The issues addressed retirement pensions of $150 per month at age 65, and eligibility of carry-over employees for pension and insurance benefits. The 1940's reflected the concentrated efforts and success of the American Labor Unions in raising the living standards of American workers.

## Unions in the 1950's

In 1950 employees voted for union shop at Pickands-Mather, Hanna, Inland Steel and C.C.I. PM miners voted in favor of the union 361-24. Hanna ballots showed 600 favor and only 44 against.

Only a one-day walkout by Hanna employees occurred in 1951. In February 1952 firms and unions argued over a wage boost for ore miners, based on the reasoning that both companies and unions had followed the wage work patterns established by steel companies. In unprecedented action, President Truman ordered the steel mills be taken over by the Secretary of Commerce in April 1952. In June 1700 production and maintenance workers in county mines went on strike. Truman's seizure of the steel industry had been ruled unconstitutional and CIO President Philip Murray had called a nation wide strike of 650,000 steelworkers. By the end of July, miners returned to their jobs, having agreed to a 16 cent per hour raise plus additional 5 cent fringe.

1953 editorials note that chances of wage increase were poor in view of the strike of 60 days, which occurred in 1952. Strikes usually were not called 2 years in a row and raises were traditionally not by cost of living, but on production. Editorial comment was "Labor without the weapon of a strike is impotent." Workers in June did receive an 8 $\frac{1}{2}$ cent per hour boost.

In 1954 in a peace pact, iron miners stayed on the job. Changes, however, began to be reveled in the area. In Forbes location as the Davidson faded, movers toted away 18 homes, 5 every week, as they were sold to occupants. Management transfers began at Pickands-Mather. Steelworkers moved their office, which had been located in the Nasser building in Iron River for 15 years to a building of their own in Dober on 19$^{th}$ street.

Union activity increased in 1956 with a substantial pay boost being sought by steelworkers. Week-end premium pay, supplemental unemployment benefits, improved insurance coverage, a union shop, additional holidays, and expanded vacation benefits were sought. Pay level at this point was $2.47 per hour. Talks on contracts continued, but in July miners were out on strike briefly.

89

In 1957 work began on the erection of a new headframe to be shared by the Homer-Wauseca. By 1958, work was slowed to a 4-day week with Hanna Co. When the Warner Mine closed, local 4532 dissolved. One source reports a strike in 1959 stretched out for 99 days, the longest steel strike in the nations' history, while another refers to steelworkers being off their jobs for 116 days. An injunction ordered men back to work, an injunction that was to expire January 16, 1960, so negotiations continued into 1960 with two major considerations—early retirement and cost of living adjustments.

1959 also marked the worst disaster of the decade. Five men, August Zucal, Ingvar Wester, Carl Rudy Anderson, Einar Johnson, and Howard Groop were killed in an explosion at the Sherwood. Talcott Shaver became a 6th victim.

So ended over 25 years of unionization with the beginning realization that the gradual closure of mines would ultimately bring a close to the industry in Iron County.

## MINERS AND UNION LEADERSHIP-*Walter C.(Ditch) Brey and Louis Passamani*

### *Louis Passamani*

The union got started in this area shortly after the Depression when people were all pressed and fed up on being pushed around. When the Steel Workers started, we got our feet down and we had a lot to gain because conditions were pretty bad in those days. Our fathers never had a chance to organize a union because they would get fired if they did. The conditions were so bad that most of them when they went to vote, had to take their instructions ballots into a dark room and copy them down at home and then when they got down to the ballot box they take the ballot out and copy it. They feared they might be discharged from their work or chased out of a company house. So personally the things that I went after were the ones my father never had.

I used to carry his dinner pail down to the dry at the Rogers Mine. At that time there wasn't such a thing as a grievance, but I could tell he had grievances in his stomach. I used to wait for the dinner pail. We always had some little things to bring home. Sometimes he would take that dinner pail and go out in the shade and eat it. Then half an hour after he would cough it up. It might have been ulcers. Nobody knew at that time. But to me, I think they were grievances that he had to swallow for fear of speaking up. Things like that there, and the conditions that we lived in. When we had a chance to organize, I was really proud of being a member of the Steel Workers. We got started up here about 1937.

Earlier efforts didn't get very far…I know, one time when I worked in the Bates Mine, the union was first started up here. We were going to take a vote whether to have an independent mining company union or to go C.I.O. The shift bosses and mining company personnel were going around in the mines and making threats to the working people, making them scared to join the union. I forget exactly the date, but they had a hearing in the Iron River town hall. The mining company lost the case that time. They were fined for threatening the union. But you never saw much about it in the *Iron River Reporter* or the headlines of the *Iron Mountain News*. But they did lose that case and the union won. After they won that case, the people started waking up. They knew they had somebody behind them.

The conditions that we were trying to improve were mostly health and safety. Then some wage increases and pensions. You know there were a lot of people in the local tried to be as democratic as they can. There are a lot of people, around twenty-five or thirty years old, who join the union to look for themselves all the time, they look for wage increases. But as you get older you start thinking about a pension. International got to live with both people the young and the old. They have a problem there. Wage increase isn't all because money can be cut in many ways when you work incentive. They can give you 15 cents an hour wage increase and with the incentive they could take back part of the fifteen they give you. You didn't gain very much through wage increases, but you did gain by insurance and safety and health

90

conditions, retirement programs. But most people don't look at that until they are over thirty. Then you start thinking about pension.

### Walter C. (Ditch) Brey

Working conditions were the big thing they fought for. I know my dad used to tell me. Most of the foreigners that came here didn't speak the language. The English could read and write the language and most of those people got the boss jobs. They took advantage of Louis's dad, my dad, all of those people. They would have a hazardous place to work and maybe the foreman wouldn't even go into the work area. We would point and tell you to go in that direction. If you didn't, you had a threat.

Workmen's compensation came later. We got involved politically, the unions did. We knew the people who were on our side and we would elect these type of persons to go to Washington to advocate workmen's compensation. Getting involved politically was important…The company always said to us that there was no need for this legislation. They would police it. But we saw the people that were carried out in baskets every day. The hazards were always there.

Naturally we always had people who leaned toward the company side because they figured they were going to better themselves, become foreman. We had this in the sixties yet before we closed. You have elements in every industry that leaned to the companies' side. The union never pressured anybody. The company would take some of our officers and offer them boss jobs. Louie talk about that experience when they called you in and offered you a foreman job.

### Louis Passamani

I came up from underground one day and they called me into the office. I said, "You got a grievance?" They said, "No, we just want to see you." They had a few guys going back and forth. I was waiting my turn. They waited until it cleared out and then they took me in the corner. They asked me, "What do you think about a shift boss job:" I said, "I don't want to be a shift boss.

### Walter Brey

They took our recording secretary and made a boss out of him. Quite a few of our union people, they turned out to be pretty good company men after while too.

We saw change…All the benefits came in—extended vacation, more liberal pensions, higher payments. The improvements were quite great over what my dad went out with—maybe $65 a month. Today they get about $325 a month. The vacations are longer. We have a ten-week vacation plus your four week regular vacation. Before maybe they had a week. The Steel Workers was a good union…When we went out on strike, we went out not only for ourselves. We went out for maybe half of the working people of the United States, different organizations. We got our raise and they automatically had to give them to the clerk in the stores and different people.

That mining companies left our area because the unions made too many demands is false. If you check the Hanna records, their quarter reports, they made money here. They told us this. Taxes weren't a problem. What the union demanded was no problem because we sat at the table. Louis and I sat at the bargaining table with them. It was a matter of phasing out the underground mines. They went into the pellet thing and there was the pure ore and all the furnaces down below were converted to oxygen type. These furnace wouldn't handle the impurities any more. You came out of these underground mines with probably a fifty or fifty five per cent iron product and the rest was all waste. No, that is false that the unions demands forced the mines to close because the company themselves told us they made a good dollars here.

Oh yes, companies had influence. They always saw to it that their people sat on city council, school boards. I ran seven times for the city commission in Iron River. I never got elected until the mining companies left. When the millage issue came up, they saw that it didn't go through because the companies pay the burden of taxes here. They always had people on the boards to advocate policy in the community. They were kind of watch dogs, too. Like I said, I never got elected.

# MINING DISASTER AT MANSFIELD-1893

On the night of September 28, the night shift at the Mansfield mine that had gone down to work could hear the river rumbling above and noticed that more water than usual was coming into the mine. No special alarm was felt because the pumps seemed to be able to keep the drifts free. At about nine o'clock, without warming, the roof of the mine collapsed and allowed the Michigamme River to plunge into the mine causing the drowning death of twenty-seven men. Not until the mine was filled did the river resume its natural course. The twenty-seven lives taken made this, the worst disaster of Iron County, even to this present day.

There were survivors of Mansfield disaster and they remembered it as a "nightmare in the dark." The men on duty at the mouth of Number One shaft felt the ground crack and tremble beneath their feet. The surface between the shaft and the river fell into the caverns below with a grinding crash. Martin Johnson, who had his leg severed in an accident at the mine a few weeks before, heard the roar of the river as it poured into the mine. He was in his home, recovering from his injury, and was unable to help any of his friends.

Frank Kiernan was at the boarding house at the time of the disaster and heard three blasts of the mine whistle, which was the prearranged emergency call for the master mechanic. After seeing the river making its way into the mine, he hurried to the boiler room where the main valves were located and shut off the steam leading to the mine. Matt Johnson, who had worked the first shift, also heard the whistle blowing and knew something was wrong. Over at the shaft, there was just a little hole about 75-feet where the river started coming in and Number One shaft had all but disappeared as the Michigamme, with a hollow roar, plunged into the mine.

Tony Baletto, the skip-tender, was standing with Frank Rocko, a night boss, at the shaft on the fourth level. They heard the crash and realized what was coming and anticipated the result. Frank heroically refused to go up in the skip until he had warned his men of the danger. He went back into the drift and perished with his men. Baletto came to the surface in the skip and was the only man who went to work on the fourth level who came out alive.

Andrew Sullivan, another night boss, was on the sixth level at the time and heard the crash above. He called to his men to follow him quickly up the ladder way. The draft caused by the cave-in extinguished their lights and the men were compelled to feel their way through the darkness. All but four men on this level reached the ladder way in safety and ascent was begun.

The men had a very hard time climbing the ladders because a torrent of water was pouring down the shaft. A distant roar and the rush of water, the flood came so fast that it is doubtful if any men in the upper levels were able to reach the shaft at all.

Fedele Cheski, head of the carpenter shop, and his wife, Angele, also rushed to the mine head to help their friends and later could still see Felix Andrizzi and Victor Johnson coming up the ladder to the surface. Johnson and Andrizzi were the last known men to reach the surface—Johnson minus his boots. Angele helped hold up homemade torches so the men could see the last ladder coming up to the surface.

A wild cry of alarm ran through the village that brought sleeping men, women and children from their beds to find a few men crawling up the ladders. Tom and William Bates were among the men rushing to the mine head to help—but to no avail. The nearest telegraph office was at Crystal Falls, six miles away, and though the Chicago Northwestern Railroad ran through Mansfield, it was only used to haul ore and bring in supplies. A courier carried the news to Crystal Falls.

A rescuing party was organized and a special train with 100 men left Crystal Falls. Horses and everything in the shape of wagons was pressed into service to help but, by that time, it was impossible that any of the entombed men could be rescued alive. Special trains were run from Florence, Wisconsin, and Crystal Falls to Mansfield so curious people could view the last resting place of twenty-seven men.

Captain Louis Aeschliman, under whose direct supervision the mining was done, said the roof of the fifth level had been shifty for several days, but nothing that the miners considered indicative of imminent danger appeared. To secure the thing, however, new timber was placed in the level on Thursday and it appeared to be perfectly safe on Thursday night. The cave-in was believed to have started on the fifth level.

C.T. Roberts was the Mine Inspector for Iron County. His investigation of the Mansfield disaster showed the cave-in to be short. Were it otherwise, it would have been only a distance of fifty feet. He was of the opinion that no loss of life would have occurred and damages would have been small if the water from the river had not rushed into the mine. *(See Mansfield Township Centennial Book 1891-1991)*

## MINING DISASTER AT AMASA-1918

"The most infamous of mining disasters in Amasa was the Porter Mine catastrophe on February 21, 1918, which claimed the lives of 17 men.

Some time before the calamity, there was a cave-in which occurred a short distance from the shaft house forming a pit 250 feet in diameter with a depth of 75 feet. There was some 10 feet of water in the hole. When this happened, all miners immediately evacuated with the exception of the pumpmen.

The mining company had anticipated the collapse of this area, for some time prior to the cave-in they had the county road commission construct a new road to the Porter Mine Location, which circumvented the danger area. However, in spite of the warning against usage of the old road, people continued to use the more direct route, and a number of school children had a narrow escape the day the earth collapsed.

Four days later, after an inspection of the mine and particular scrutiny of the bulkheads on the 200, 300, and 400 foot levels, the men were called to work and operations were resumed.

The aforementioned bulkheads were built of concrete and were a precautionary measure used to prevent the anticipated sloughing of water, mud and sand into the shaft. These bulkheads were 6 feet thick and located 70 feet from the shaft on the 200 and 300 foot levels and 125 feet from the shaft on the 400 foot level. It was believed that these bulkheads would hold back any pressure from the expected open pit.

At noon Thursday, February 21, the miners came to surface to eat their lunches in the "dry." Ten men were aboard the first cage to go down into the shaft after the lunch period, and on the second trip nine men were being lowered when there was a rush of water and sand into the shaft from the 200' level which sent the cage and men plunging to the bottom of the mine, some 550 feet, despite the frantic efforts of the hoistman to stop the cage.

Had the accident occurred ten minutes sooner, no one would have been injured; had it happened half an hour later, all of the men on that shift, about 100, would have been caught like rats in a trap and drowned.

Here is the story given by Alfred Erickson, a Crystal Falls miner who had been waiting his turn to descend into the mine.

"Dinner was over and the men started to descend to work about 12:30. Two pumpmen were in the mine; one on the lower level and one on the third level where the top pump was located.

One cage of men descended. The lander says that four men were on the cage. The cage came up and loaded the second time. The lander says nine men were on it. I didn't count them, so I can't say for sure just how many men were on it.

When the second cage got down as far as the third level, we, who were standing at the shaft, noticed that there was something wrong with the cage. The brakeman noticed it also and tried to stop it by putting on the brake, but was unable to hold it and the cage went right to the bottom before it stopped.

One man ran over to the pit and yelled back that the water was going down. We then knew what was wrong. I think that the run of sand and water lasted about 15 minutes. Three men came up the shaft, one the

93

pumpman from the third level. One of the men who came up had nothing left of his clothing but a shirt, the sand and water had ripped everything from him. I can remember but one of the men, Axel West of Balsam. He came up minus his shoes, which had been stripped from his feet by the falling water.

We could hear no noise as the rush of water was too far down in the shaft. We did hear the men who got up as they neared the surface.

A number of us immediately went down the shaft. I got as far down as the third level. From there down the ladderway was blocked and had not been cleared when I left the mine about six o'clock.

When we got down to the third level, we found that all the water had drained out and that everything was quiet. I went into the drift where the bulkhead was and found that there was about two feet of sand in the bottom. The water had all drained out of the sand and it was hard so we could get in.

The cage and one skip were fast upon the bottom. The rope of the other skip was cut and the skip was lowered down as possible, but it got wedged and couldn't go all the way down.

One man was stepping onto the second cage when he thought of two picks he had taken up to have sharpened, so he stepped off just as it was about to descend and his life was thereby saved."

Rescue efforts were begun immediately, but were futile. Four days later a second run of water and sand stopped all rescue work. It was then that a man on watch at the open pit noticed water leaving the pit. He ran to the shaft and rapped on the pipes, a signal of impending danger, and hearing the signal, the men underground ran to the waiting skip and were brought to surface.

It was several weeks before the bodies of all the victims were recovered from the mine. *(See Amasa, Michigan by Roy Koski.)*

\*\*\*\*\*\*\*\*\*\*

## THE FURNACE AND KILNS—PHOTOGRAPH AND HISTORY

Early Iron River. Charcoal kilns on Minckler Hill. Furnace was located at left and front.

94

IRON RIVER FURNACE COMPANY UNPROFITABLE VENTURE...With the arrival of the railroad into Iron River in the autumn of 1882, the area was stirred into renewed activity. The nation was enjoying moderate prosperity at the moment, for the reconstruction years of the Civil War had been hurdled and industrial expansion was general throughout the land.

Thus in the year 1883; there came to Iron River a new enterprise known as the Iron River Furnace Company, which was organized for the specific purpose of smelting the ores of the Nanaimo Mine...

The organizers of the company were the Hewitt Iron Mining Company of which John S. McDonald was president and John Spence, secretary;-this company operated the Nanaimo Mine. Others interested were William H. Wells, Paul Minckler, Benjamin Philbrick, Edward Foster, Henry Woessner and David McIntyre. With the exception of Minckler, a local man, the company was controlled by outside capitalists and the company headquarters were at Fond du Lac, Wisconsin.

The site for the plant was a twenty-acre tract of the John Sipschen homestead lands north of the river and northeast of the mine workings. The easterly ten acres was set aside for the furnace plant and the westerly half was platted as a housing project for employees. Part of the latter half was later incorporated into the J.J.Sipschen First Addition to the Village of Iron River and the site of the former furnace later was occupied by the Jean mill.

Actual construction was begun January 1,1884. It was completed in due time with much of the equipment used being salvaged material from a furnace that was destroyed by fire at Munising. The stack was fifty-six feet high and had a base diameter of eleven feet. A trestle was constructed from the mine to carry the ore over the river to the plant and eight charcoal kilns were built on the hillside north of the furnace.

The venture later rose to the sizeable figure of $106,000 but the company soon encountered financial difficulties. A bond issue of eighty bonds in $500 denominations was floated to complete the project. A Tennessee capitalist named Ries was the largest investor and the Chicago & Northwestern Railroad among others, was one of the smaller ones.

The kilns were constructed by Robert Flanherty and Walter Lovelace and failing to get payment for this work by 1887, secured a lien on the property.

Following an unprofitable operation of several years the plant was leased to L. S. Hoyt of Pennsylvania and a Rogers and Brown of Cincinnati, Ohio for the rental sum of fifty cents per gross ton of pig iron produced. This also failed and upon expiration of their lease April 1, 1888, the plant closed . . .

During the operation there were several dwellings and a store building erected west of the plant. Upon dissolvation of the company, these were removed into the village proper.

A more detailed history on the furnace is to found in the History of Iron County, which was compiled and written by Jack Hill.

# PRODUCTION – NUMBER OF ACCIDENTS
## TONNAGE PER FATALITY FROM 1923 to 1969

| Year | Production | Total No. Employees | Total of Accidents | Total of Fatalities | Tonnage per Fatality | No. Mines Producing |
|---|---|---|---|---|---|---|
| 1923 | 3,196,446 | 3,323 | 301 | 4 | 799,112 | 25 |
| 1924 | 2,844,656 | 2,819.87 | 457 | 9 | 316,073 | 27 |
| 1925 | 3,412,046 | 2,695 | 444 | 8 | 426,506 | 26 |
| 1926 | 4,077,701 | 2,654.7 | 415 | 7 | 582,529 | 25 |
| 1927 | 4,357,603 | 2,611.38 | 367 | 7 | 622,515 | 24 |
| 1928 | 4,126,198 | 2,452 | 219 | 6 | 687,700 | 25 |
| 1929 | 3,772,288 | 2,287 | 148 | 11 | 342,935 | 22 |
| 1930 | 3,800,098 | 2,265 | 101 | 8 | 475,012 | 28 |
| 1931 | 1,962,107 | 1,559 | 57 | 2 | 981,053 | 21 |
| 1932 | 837,811 | 1,271 | 25 | 1 | 837,811 | 15 |
| 1933 | 480,280 | 1,085* | 16 | 0 | — | 12 |
| 1934 | 710,646 | 1,148* | 25 | 1 | 710,646 | 9 |
| 1935 | 455,551 | 861 | 15 | 0 | — | 8 |
| 1936 | 1,056,940 | 813** | 31 | 2 | 528,470 | 10 |
| 1937 | 1,638,091 | 1,193** | 36 | 0 | — | 12 |
| 1938 | 1,411,457 | 867 | 31 | 2 | 705,729 | 12 |
| 1939 | 1,168,409 | 1,145 | 19 | 0 | — | 9 |
| 1940 | 1,481,331 | 1,167 | 37 | 2 | 740,666 | 10 |
| 1941 | 1,942,840 | 1,581 | 55 | 1 | 1,942,840 | 13 |
| 1942 | 2,870,184 | 2,025 | 115 | 4 | 717,546 | 15 |
| 1943 | 4,043,118 | 2,331 | 211 | 11 | 367,556 | 17 |
| 1944 | 4,883,054 | 2,010 | 162 | 8 | 610,382 | 16 |
| 1945 | 3,430,830 | 1,634 | 75 | 0 | — | 14 |
| 1946 | 3,483,368 | 1,601 | 59 | 2 | 1,741,684 | 14 |
| 1947 | 2,588,854 | 1,866 | 81 | 1 | 2,588,854 | 13 |
| 1948 | 3,521,034 | 1,729 | 62 | 3 | 1,173,679 | 12 |
| 1949 | 4,147,127 | 1,836 | 63 | 3 | 1,382,376 | 11 |
| 1950 | 3,439,743 | 1,745 | 42 | 2 | 1,719,872 | 12 |
| 1951 | 3,944,920 | 2,029 | 44 | 2 | 1,972,460 | 12 |
| 1952 | 4,864,310 | 2,021.75 | 48 | 8 | 608,039 | 13 |
| 1953 | 3,868,493 | 2,118 | 57 | 1 | 3,868,493 | 14 |
| 1954 | 4,458,860 | 2,060.5 | 45 | 1 | 4,458,860 | 15 |
| 1955 | 3,551,933 | 1,617 | 50 | 1 | 3,551,993 | 13 |
| 1956 | 4,292,201 | 1,883 | 66 | 2 | 2,146,101 | 11 |
| 1957 | 4,413,414 | 1,773** | 41 | 2 | 2,206,707 | 10 |
| 1958 | 2,932,272 | 1,451 | 34 | 7 | 418,896 | 7 |
| 1959 | 2,452,379 | 1,545 | 18 | 0 | — | 8 |
| 1960 | 3,326,177 | 1,412 | 43 | 1 | 3,326,177 | 8 |
| 1961 | 3,224,576 | 1,192 | 31 | 1 | 3,224,576 | 7 |
| 1962 | 2,498,731 | 1,023 | 40 | 1 | 2,498,731 | 7 |
| 1963 | 2,709,151 | 1,017 | 37 | 0 | — | 5 |
| 1964 | 2,888,432 | 985 | 45 | 0 | — | 5 |
| 1965 | 2,980,194 | 909 | 42 | 2 | 1,460,047 | 5 |
| 1966 | 2,960,069 | 789 | 64 | 1 | 2,960,069 | 5 |
| 1967 | 2,170,972 | 665 | 61 | 1 | 2,170,972 | 4 |
| 1968 | 1,782,937 | 612 | 24 | 1 | 1,782,937 | 4 |
| 1969 | 403,419 | 106 | 7 | 0 | — | 1 |

*  Part Time          **  Staggered

# LIST OF MEN WHO GAVE THEIR LIVES IN THE MINES

## *FORWARD*

Deaths recorded on the following lists and on the Memorial in the Iron County Museum Mining Memorial Hall have been gathered from several sources, but primarily from Mining Inspector reports that were available. The Office of mining inspector was first created in 1889. The first written annual report still in existence dates September 30,1900—September 30,1901, at which time there were 21 mines operating and an average of 1455 men working. A total of ten fatalities occurred in the year, occurring in the following mines: Great Western—1, Riverton—1, Columbia—1, Mansfield—2, Crystal Falls—1, Hilltop—1. Reports listed instant fatalities as opposed to total deaths—12.

The task of accumulating names was difficult when no mining inspector reports were found. Missing were the earliest years 1889-1900, and 1914-1915, 1916-1917, 1917-1918, 1919-1920.

**ALPHA (1903)**

**ARMENIA (1889-1914)** *Angus Smith or Smith Mine*
LaCrosse, Fames-1901

**BAKER (1909-1915)**
Lampa, Elmer-1909
Sinatek (Swiatch), John-1910
Breoi, Isidore-1910
Sorenski (Smazynski), George-1910
Konrackie, Mike-1913
Swatch, Andrew-1915

**BALKAN (1917-1942)** *Later combined with Judson*
Bevello, Dominio (Domenico)–1914
Rossi, Batiste (a) –1914
Battan, Batiste (a) –1914
Pallaerd, Antonio (Pallaera, Victorio)–1914
Macki (e), Jack (John)–1914
Radatoria (ric), Mitar-1914
Boscele, Antonio-1914
Kuusio, John-1916
Franki, Nick-1919

**BALTIC (1901-1950)**
Hill, John–1903
Tegronien (Petronich), August-1905
Tegronien (Petronich), George-1905
Farley, John-1905
Mydtling, John-1905
Priedicel,(Prudice), Richard-1905
Rundquist, Ole-1905
Jacobson, Charles-1906
Barka, John-1906
Ruhanan (Riikonen), Sam-1907
Alperi (Alpia), Jalmar-1908
Shubat, Frank-1909
Sgagers, Angelo-1909
Mentose, Ivan-1912
Adzima, George-1920

**BATES (1915-1947)**
Wertane, Eli-1913
Unknown-7/1915

Lartignaro, Joe-1919
Yakel, William-1921
Erickson, Arthur E.-1919
Anderson, Oscar-1929
Lovince, Steve-1930
Barry, James-1936
Koski, William-1940
Major, Nick-1944

**BENGAL (1913-1963)** *Combined with Tully, Cannon later years*
Evanoff, George-1923
Bolon, Frank-1928
Colien, James-1943
Smith, Leo-1952

**BERKSHIRE (1908-1950)**
Buddle, Capt. John-1909
Nelson, John-1925

**BETA (1887-1941)**
Pedni, Romano-1905

**BOOK (1943-1957)**
Struckel, John J.-1943
Kelly, Alman A.-1946
Lepisto, Niilo A.-1947
Kermeen, William J.-1949
Groeneveld, Caesar-1956

**BRIAR HILL**
Skorjera, Josef-1892

**BRISTOL (1890-1969)**
    *Claire,(earlier combined with Youngstown, 1882-1897)*
Holm, William-1899
Krafty, William-1899
Unknown-1902
Unknown-1902
Storm, Edward-1902
Oberg, John-1903
Rosenlof, John-1903
Bacbiana (Backman), John-1903
Zebren (c)(s)ki, Frank-1904
Granville, William-1904

Tambarin (a) (o), Massino-1904
Aspholin, Emil-1905
Matson,Oscar-1905
Koski, John-1905
Hill, Matt-1906
Borsky, Lawrence-1906
Erickson, Gus-1906
Fors, John-1906
Ceserri, Pesenato-1906
Anderson, John A.-1907
Maki (Macky), Oscar H.-1907
Katt (a) (e)lla, Jack (Kataka, Jake)-1908
Pellizari, Michols-1909
Laselle, John-1909
Niemi (Nemini), Charles (Nat)-1911
Goldman (Gullman), Victor-1911
Gustafson, Fred-1912
Johnson, August-1913
Forsman, Charles-1913
Jacobson, Erik-1915
Hegstrom, Arthur-1918
Maki, Matt-1923
Martinson, John-1928
Bjork, Edward-1929
McMullen, Walter-1966

**BUCK (1901-1967)**
Lohrey, Walter-1929
Curnow, Wilfred-1932
Youngell, Ed-1941
Bucakowski, John-1943
Johnson, John A.-1944
Shubat, Albert-1950
Carne, Josiah H.-1950
Westphal, Albert-1951
D'Agostino, Enrico-1954
Blazina, Joseph-1954

**CANNON (1952-1963)**
Schinderle, Rudolph C.-1956
Penkivech, Michael P.-1957
Koski (y), John W.-1958
Lundwall, Lloyd L.-1958

**CARDIFF (1919-1923)**

**CARENTER (1913-1928)**
Krystnick, John-1914
Saari, Thomas-1915
Soline (Suline), Victor-1915
Herpa, Herman-1917
Carolo, Dominic-1918
Sartori, Joe-1919
Zambrosky, Martin-1919
Montagna, Virgil-1919
Tabecca, Frank-1919
Finadri, Serafino-1919
Marana, Mike-1920
Polari, Isaac-1923

**CASPIAN (1903-1932)**
Fairino, Robert-1906
Popnutny, Andrew-1906
Hill, Edward-1907
Malla, Joe-1907
Mottati (Motatti), Goul (Joseph)-1909
Evanoff, Tony-1915
Kubba (Kato/Kuta), Joseph-1915
Bevilacqua, Anton-1919
Di Bella, Peter-1919
Rosa, Joseph-1924

**CAYIA (1952)**

**CHATHAM (1907-1920)**
Smith, Stanley-1908
Kassha, Stanley-1908
Teuha, Chas. –1913
Kolehma, Fred-1913

**CHICAGOAN (1909-1922)**
Ezap, John-1912

**COLUMBIA (1882-1905,1941-1950)**
Einswriler, John-1895
Povlinka (Pablinco), John-1896
Pewarmic, John-1896
Swanson, Alex-1898
Unknown-1901
Helak (Helock), Peter-1902

**CORRY (1922-1928)**
Gilbert, G.-(1911 exploration)

**CORTLAND (1912-1914)**

**COTTRELL (1915-1916)**

**CRYSTAL FALLS (1882-1913)**
Waine, John-1892
Nelson, Charles-1896
Donati, Antonio-1887
Castellano, George-1898
Jacobson, John-1900
Macki, George-1900
Flemming, Isaac-1901
Hikizas (Hiskigas), Lamme (Lainne)-1902
Unknown-3/24/1902
Carmini (Carohimo/Coronimo), Dominick-1902
Palmi (Peolio), Jacob (Jackob)-1902
Mattson, Matt-1902
Storm, Herman-1902
Bodnar (Buduon), Andrew-1902
Jill (Gili), Robert-1903
Alueta (Alenti), Louis-1903

Fernquist (Franquist), Carl (Charles)-1903
Storm, Warner (Wiener)-1903
Minesuary, Frank-1904

**DAVIDSON GROUP** *Wapama*
        *(No.1,2,3 1911-1953) (No. 4 1913-1921)*
Koski, Sam-1913 (No.2)
Randala, Nester-1915 (No.1)
Eckman, Elmer-1928
Tomish (Tomljenovic), Tony-1930
Karvala, William-1949
Kmichik, Stanley-1952
Sloat, Lionel-1952
Possanza, Fred-1952
Turcotte, Henry-1952
Macky, Werner-1952

**DELPHIC (1883-1896)**

**DELTA (1920-1925)**

**DOBER**
Winter, Paul-1902
Moore, George-1907
Erickson, William-1907
Roseland, Frank-1907
Lind, William-1907
Selikki (Sylak), George-1910
Anderson, Konstanti-1911
Maki, Abel-1911
Berganini, Caesar-1912

**DUNN (1887-1915)**
Kassock, George-1887
Domenica, Saratorio-1888
Sporatablia, Joseph-1888
Coval, Dominici-1889
Price, Jacob-1891
Cavosa, Gabriele-1892
Chamourney, Josef-1892
Echer, Ignazio-1895
Antia (Autia), Jacob-1901
Larson, Ed-1905
Belle, Nicholas-1906
Talarico, Frank-1906
Berg, John-1907
Bjorki, John-1907
Bataties, John-1907
Larson, (Albin) Carl-1910
Johnson, Charles (Carl/Claus)-1910
Sensiba (Sausiba), Peter-1910
Mackie, Alex-1911
Franciso, John (Joseph)-1911
Rajamaki, Abel-1911
Rundin, Gust-1912
Gustafson, Adolph-1912

**FOGARTY (1907-1949)**
Peterson, Ernest-1909
Rullcoski (Rulkowski), Jake-1911

**FORBES (1912-1946)**
Sleeman, William-1913
King, Grandville-1915
Tuomi, Alex-1924
Lahti, John-1925
Anderson, August-1926
Zipkowski, Joe-1928
Maki, Simon-1928
Beckman, August-1928

**FORTUNE LAKE (1953-1956)**

**GENESEE (1902-1935)**
Tuominen, Kalli (Charles)-1929
Ma(e)tsavage, Joseph-1929

**GIBSON (1885-1911)**
Mangensen (Magnuson), Gust-1908
Rampeleto, Peter-1910

**GREAT WESTERN (1882-1915)**
Erickson, John-1887
Hooper, William (Capt.)-1890
Wassuri, Abraham-1891
Rundbacka, Gust-1891
Johson, Matt-1891
Kammerer, John, Jr.-1899
Unknown 11/21/1900
Unknown 2/1901
Johnson, John-1901
Suckahusky, John-1903
Keniska (Kasska), Andrew-1903
Rentamiki (Lindimaiki), Matt-1907
Gimbick, Rugen-1907
Schrisa, Frank-1907
Bregger, William H.-1909
Bowden (Boroden, William), W.J.-1909

**HEMLOCK (1891-1938)**
Tamanin, Eugenio-1892
Mollok -John M.-1897
Roberts, Frederick-1898
Sorey, Andrew-1898
Scovera, Joseph-1898
Brown, Frank-1899
Koronok, Joseph-1899
Mahata, Morrie-1901
Juntasa, George-1901
Unknown-3/20/1902
Zelesnick, Steve-1902
Lautomus, Nicholas-1902
Anderson, Peter-1903

Kuni, John-1904
Koylar (Kujolo/Kujala), Herman-1903
Hantala, John-1904
Lalita, Henry-1906
Hechim, August-1906
Giddosh, Joe-1906
Wertenen, Jacob-1907
Wirtava, Isaac-1907
Manilla, Peter-1908
Walin (Walline), Hjalmar-1908
Swanson, Otto-1909
Koylar, Herman-1909
Odreso, Joe-1910
Hartman, Frank-1910
Rachinski, Zegmund-1910
Abourisi (Oderisi, John) Joseph-1910

**HIAWATHA**
     *(No. 1, 1893-1950) (No. 2, 1935-1966)*
Mahlstrom, John-1903
Esson, John-1903
Hill, Matt-1906
Brosky, Lawrence-1906
Fors, John-1906
Erickson, Gust-1906
Quanstrom, Isadore-1908
Andriolli (Nedrolli), Adolph-1909
Helein (Hebun/Hebein), Lorenz-1910
Klook, Walter-1910
Philstrom, (Kelstrom/Kjelstrom) Otto-1911
Makoski, George-1914
Pretroski, Chester-1930
Dennis, Mike-1945
Broslavick, Walter-1948
Fredrickson, Edwin-1951
Fittante, Joseph-1952
Benishek, Joseph W.-1957

**HILLTOP (1899-1919)**
Carlson, John-1901

**HOLLISTER (1890-1914)**
Johnson, Andrew-1908

**HOMER (1914-1969)**
Angeli, Sam (Sesinio)-1916
Hendrickson, Frankie-1917
Hendrickson, Isaac-1917
Greig, James-1917
Domino (Dominico, Santa-1918
Munnici, Melcharde-1924
Aho, Onni-1924
Rosiak, Steve-1924
Kuusisto, Emil-1924
Salmi, William-1925
Muckki, George-1925

Mandolini, Dominic-1927
Wytonick, John-1927
O'Connor, William-1928
Today,John-1936
Spoke, Daniel-1938
LeClair, David-1938
Petroff, Mike-1940
Kasprowski, Karlo-1941
Petsin, George-1944
Komblevicz, Joseph-1946
Barry, Henry J.-1952
Garland, Winton S.-1958
Zaiki, Donald-1958
Pakula, Francis T.-1958
Zukowski, Benjamin-1967

**HOPE (1892-1903)**
Maki, Gus(t)-1902
Hill, Wanta-1902

**HURON**
Snosky, Andrew-2/7/1901

**IRON RIVER** *(Stambaugh) (Riverton Group)*
Unknown-9/17/1885
Wills, Joseph-1889
Gerteen, Joseph-1889
Rymse, Leon-1889
Zeni, Luigi-1890
Palmer, Charles-1890
Johnson, Charles-1890
Henrickson, Isaac

**ISABELLA**
Westerberg, John O.-1888

**JAMES (1907-1953)** *Osana*
Terzone, Sante-1911
Webb, William-1924
Champion, Clarence-1924
Mattiolli,Sabatino-1928
Rometti, Silvio-1928
Berlin, Charles-1929
Messon, Joseph-1943
Carlson, Oscar-1943
Holmes, Victor 1943
Pisoni, Candido-1943

**JONES-LAUGHLIN** *Forbes*
Cornowski, Matt-1926

**JUDSON 1917-1942** *Combined with Balkan*
Franki, Nick-1919
Kiepes (Kapes), Walter-1920
Kaneunen (Kaneusen), Hjalmer-1920
Hager, John-1921

Johnson, Victor-1925
Suber, John-1925
Mottes, Louis-1921
Fagotti, Alex-1926
Rodnor, Steve-1928
Pappan, Felix-1928
Trudell, Ambose-1930
Hakkanen, Joe-1931

**KIMBALL (1907-1915)**
Oyia, Gust-1907

**KONWINSKI** *See Wauseca*

**LAMONT (1889-1910)** *Monitor*
Backman, John-1891 Monitor
Berry, James-1890 Monitor
Bocan, ?-1899 Monitor
Macki (Hyavatti), Solomon-1899
Lymon, John-1900
Bacon (Bocan), Louis-1902 Lamont
Paavela (Paavola/Parvo), Jacob-1903 Lamont

**LAWRENCE (1920-1956)** *Wilkinson*

**LINCOLN (1891-1909)**
Erickson, Oscar-1891
Mangerson, John-1900

**McDONALD (1908-1913)**
Ternico, Dominic (Tassoniero, Dominick)-1913

**MANSFIELD (1890-1913)**
Barry, James-1890
Tiderman, Frank-1890
Franceschini, Luigi-1891
Romero, Julio-1891
Bonte, Martin-1891
Decampi, Leopold-1892
Paoli (Pauli), August-1892
Bybas, Thomas-1892
Pumermeir (Pampimane), Attilio-1892
Bonadimani (Bondi), William (Guglialmo)-1892
Passamoni, Giuseppe (Joseph)-1893
Hendrickson, August-1893
Zadra , Victor (Vitore)-1893
*THE 1893 DISASTER*
Arcangelo, Chris
Constanti, O.D.
Begula (Benila/Regula), John
Carlson, Ole
Cologno, August
Fontane, Nicolo
Fortinati, Bosc
Harrington, Mike
Holmstrom, John

Johnson, Frank
Johnson, Sam
Johnson, Swan
Kola (Colla/Kella/Kullar), Jacob
Kirrppu (Kirrpp), John
Lundquist (Lindquist), Oscar
Negri (Negni), Celesti
Pearce (Pierce), W. H.
Peters (Petter), Sam
Pohl (Polsr), Charles
Randala, John
Rocko, Frank
Stefano, Anton (Sepano, August)
Strongman, James
Torresani, Al
Turg (Turry), Pete
Warner, John
Zadra, Vigilio (Vigillis)
Zadro, Sheltmo (Shelimo)
Companier, Joseph-1893
Peterson, Charles-1898
Richards, Richard-1898
Hakala, Matti-1899
Delemaurenti, Massian-1899
Maricfineo, Bolerto-1899
Mills, Otto-1901
Genduso, Joseph-1901
Paporas, Nicolas-1901
Koski, Alex-1903
Kaski, Eric-1903
Benvenuti, Benamino-1906
Biclcuin (Biclcuim/Biclinin), Omfrey-1906
Walter, William-1906
Osterby, Alex-1906
Le Conati (LeBonati/LeBorati), August (Augus)-1907
Beouamto, Buramio-1908
Johnson, Andrew-1908
Kivinen (Kivvinnen), Hjalmar (Yalmar)-1911
Kanfas (Kangas), Vina-1915

**MANGANITE**
Comsy, Samuel-1890

**MASTODON (1882-1942)**
     **and SOUTH MASTODON (1887-1890)**
Serattil, Domenico-1888
Springer, Capt. Wilfred O.-1890
Eldund, Andrew-1890
Kalafut, Andreas (Andrew)-1892

**MICHIGAN (1893-1916)**
Matson (Mattson), John-1905
Leyn, Caesar-1912

**MONONGAHELA (1901-1943)**
Richards, William-1921
Kinsman, James-1921
Thomas, Robert-1923

**NANAIMO (1882-1908)**
Constantini, Martini-1905
Santi, Leoni-1911

**NORTH ARMENIA (1889-1914)**
Mackie, Sam-1909

**ODGERS (1916-1935)**
Giske (Geske), Arthur-1921
Nichols, Richard-1926

**PAINT RIVER (1882-1913)** *Fairbanks*
Ryan, James C.-1887
Trelour, Harry-1887

**PORTER (1914-1927)**
*1918 DISASTER*
Alonki (Alonke/Alonkin), Gabriel
Bokoski (Grokosky), Theodore
Erickson, E. (Erick)
Ellis, John (Jack)
Gorman, Joseph (German, Joe)
Isaacson, Isaac (Leonard)
Isotalo, Matt
Johnson, John A.
Johnson, Oscar
Kari (Kaie), Jacob (Jarl)
Kanvils (Kniivila), Charles
Kivela, C.
Kivimaki (Kivimacki/Kurmaki), Victor
Rudis (Rudie), Jim (James)
Sand (Sands), Andrew
Sartori (Satoria), John
Surimak (Surnick/Surinack), Steve

Ketola (Kotoa), Alex-1922
Sturvist (Schurdist), Nestor-1922
Jaskalla, Oscar (Otto)-1922

**RAVENNA-PRICKETT (1911-1943)**

**RED ROCK EXPLORATION**
Drake (Drage), Mono (Mons)-1909
Lahti, Alex-1916
Pokkari, Andrew-1916

**RICHARDS (1913-1927)** *Dunn* -- **RIVERTON (1882-1937)**
Unknown 2/1901
Unknown 8/2/1901
Hultman, Gust-1902
Asplund, Andrew-1902
Vingo (Winzo), Adam-1905
Brandish, Stanley-1913
Conta, Henry-1925

**ROGERS (1914-1945)**
Dunic, Alex-1923
Geissler, Fred-1926
Windsor, Eugene-1929

**SHAFER**
Nevlin, John-1890
Waine, John-1892

**SHERIDAN (1889-1900)**

**SHERWOOD (1931-1978)**
Nye, Raymond-1943
Roman, Arne O.-1944
Mongiat, Daniel-1944
Groop, Wallace-1948
Groop, Howard-1959
Johnson, Einar-1959
Shaver, Talcott A. Jr.-1959
Wester, Ingvar D.-1959
Zucal, August J.-1959
Anderson, Carl R.-1959
Verville, Louis-1966
Peruzzi,George-1977

**SPIES (1916-1955)** *Virgil*
Kopenski, Frank-1921
Michell, Thomas-1926
Vivian, John-1940
Filipczuk, Frank-1943
Puskala, John-1944

**TOBIN (1901-1962)**
Seppela, Nikolai-1902
Baptista, John-1903
Gustman (Gastman), Matt-1903
Franere (Franeres), Pete-1903
Dean, Edwin (Edward) -1903
Conshove, Frank-1904
Vaushaua (Vanshauae), Frank-1904
Hanson, John-1904
Julha (Jylha/Jyllia), Matt-1904
Tremitath (Tremitah), Joe-1904
Opermaki (Ohe-macki), Mike-1906
Solomon, Sam-1906
Freeman, Henry-1908
Macki, John-1908
Breontior (Bertoni), Joseph-1908
Lippi, Jukki-1909
Mackie, Solomon-1910
Warditz, Joe-1911
Mausaja (Manija), Frank-1916
Hill, Isaac-1918
Matsuga (Macerga), Joe-1918
Socha (Soha), Mike-1924
Dahl, John-1924
Hartung, Bert-1925
Lilijgren, Carl-1925
Kallio, Anton-1933
Collicelli, Guiseppe-1942
Kullberg, Sigard-1943
Pintarelli, Ernest-1943
Johnson, Emil-1962

**TULLY (1910-1950)**
Mitchell, Alfred-1910
Hepola, Knosta-1911
Erickson, Herman-1915
Pucci, Raffael-1915
Marko, Nick-1918
Kosky, Jack-1918
Pavolich, Nick-1918

**VIRGIL (WITH SPIES) (1912-1946)**
Grude, Eurico-1913

**WICKWIRE (1911-1917)**
Peterson, Peter G.-1913

**WARNER (1915-1957)**
Lahti, Alex-1916
Pokkari, Andrew-1916
Lodrigo, Anton-1917
Delick, Peter-1924
Wertinen, Frank-1926
Gustafson, Andrew-1916
Hill, Arne-1926

**WAUSECA (1926-1969)** *Aronson*
Andree, Kenneth-1948
Cascioli, Bruno-1950
Frederickson, Edwin G.-1951
Smith, Leo-1952
Anderson, Russel C.-1956
Flancher, John-1960
Ridolphi, Frank-1963
Dzarnowski, Peter-1965
Dinco, Alfred-1967

**YOUNGS (1905-1928)**
Convenski, Joe-1906
Convenski, Adam-1906
Finnila (Finnilar)-John C. -1907
Weilupsky, Walter-1907
Jarhi, Mike-1909
Lashie, Martin-1909
Berina (Berini/Buorusi), Tony-1910
Romitta (Ranitta), Peitro (Peter)-1911
Contarta, Santo-1911
Spore, Sam-1911
Malmquist, Arnold-1913
Broskovetz, Julius-1916
Unknown-1916

**YOUNGSTOWN (1882-1897)** *See Bristol*
Sjoberg, John-1887
Ball, Capt. Thomas Jr.-1887

**ZIMMERMAN (1907-1950)**
Polosach, George-1912
Matteo, Gasperi-1912
Campana, John-1912
Nordi, Joseph-1915
Smith, Adam-1921
Lepisto, Carlo-1926
Osterlund, Walter-1930
Pykari, Anti-1930
Dobson, Matt-1942
Turbessi, Biagio-1943
Knevilla, Jack-1943
D'Agostini, Enrico-1954

# THE LANGUAGE OF THE MINER

| | |
|---|---|
| **Back:** | That part of a drift which is above. |
| **Barricade:** | A fence or other obstruction to prevent persons from entering a danger area. |
| **Bed rock:** | The solid rock underlying glacial and alluvial deposits. |
| **Bench:** | A ledge extending at right angles from sub levels into the stope. |
| **Beneficiation:** | Any operation that improves either the iron content or the physical structure of an iron ore. |
| **Blasting:** | The operation of breaking rock or ore by means of explosives. |
| **Bomb:** | A packet of dynamite used to break large chunks of ore. |
| **Branch:** | A short raise. |
| **Brattice:** | A partition used to regulate mine air. |
| **Breast:** | The face of a working place. |
| **Bulkhead:** | A tight partition for protection against water, fire or gas. |
| **Cage:** | A conveyance for hoisting and lowering men and materials in a mine. It slides between guides in the shaft and is provided with a safety clutch, engaging an automatic device for preventing the fall of the cage should the supporting cable break. |

| Camelback: | An automatic car dumping device. |
|---|---|
| Capping: | Rock above the ore. |
| Collar: | The mouth of the mine shaft. |
| Cribbing: | Timber used in raises. |
| Dead end: | An entry not connected with other mine workings. |
| Diamond drilling: | The process of exploring unknown ground by using a diamond headed drill to remove a core for examination. |
| Dike: | A long thin body of igneous rock that has entered a fissure in older rocks. Iron ore is generally found on or near dikes. |
| Dog hole: | A small untimbered sub-level drift. |
| Downcast: | A shaft through which air is drawn or forced into a mine. |
| Drift: | A horizontal passage or tunnel underground. |
| Drilling: | The use of pneumatic tools to bore holes in advancing a heading in ore or rock or to break ore. |
| Dry: | A building where employees change clothes, wash, and prepare to go to work. Also contains lamproom, and mine rescue room. |
| Engine house: | A building containing hoisting and electric power equipment. |
| Escapeway: | An opening through which miners may leave the mine if the ordinary exit is obstructed. |
| Fault: | A fracture of the strata breaking the continuity of the rock or ore formation. |
| Foot wall: | The formation underlying an ore body. |
| Forepole: | To drive poles horizontally ahead of the working face to prevent caving of the roof or side. |
| Gang: | A crew of miners. |
| Gob: | Waste material that fills the void when ore is extracted in the caving method. |
| Grizzly: | An iron grating over a raise or pocket to size chunks and guard mine openings. |
| Hanging wall: | The upper wall of an inclined ore body. |
| Haulage: | The drawing or conveying, in cars or otherwise, of the produce of the mine from the place where it is mined to the place where it is to be hoisted or stored. |
| Headframe: | A structure erected over a shaft to carry the sheaves over which the cable runs for hoisting the cage and skips. Also contains skip dump, pan conveyor, shaker screen, crushers, conveyor belts, loading bins, and a landing through which ore, rock, materials and supplies are taken in and out of the mine. |
| Jackhammer: | A pneumatic drilling machine. |
| Jasper-Taconite: | A local name for low grade iron ores. Jasper commonly refers to the lean iron ores in the Michigan iron ranges and taconite the lean iron ores in the Minnesota ranges. |
| Jumbo: | A mine truck on which several Water Leyner drill machines are mounted to drill rock heading on main levels. |
| Lagging: | Small split timbers placed over caps or behind posts to prevent fragments of rock from falling through. |
| Level: | A horizontal passage or drift into or in a mine. It is customary to work mines by levels at regular intervals in depth, numbered in their order below the collar. A level consists of drifts, and cross cuts. |
| Lifter: | Angle irons spiked to timber posts for supporting staging when lifting timbers. |
| Lining set: | A set of timber installed adjacent to an original timber set for additional support. |
| Loose: | Unsupported fractured ground clinging to the formation. |
| Missed hole: | A drill hole containing an explosive charge that has failed to explode. |

| | |
|---|---|
| **Mucking:** | The operation of moving broken ground by an electric or air hoist and scraper, an air loader, or by hand shoveling. |
| **Mud cap:** | A charge of dynamite fired in contact with the surface of a rock after being covered with wet mud. |
| **Pentice:** | A cover of native rock or timbers for the protection of men in shaft sinking. |
| **Pillar:** | A piece of ground left to support the roof or hanging wall. |
| **Raise:** | An opening, like a shaft, made in the back of a level to reach a level above. |
| **Rock burst:** | Fracture of rock strata. |
| **Rock dump:** | A place for the disposal of waste rock extracted during the course of mining operations. |
| **Shaft:** | An excavation of limited area, compared with its depth, made for finding or mining ore, raising water, or rock, and hoisting and lowering men and material or ventilating underground workings. |
| **Shaft station:** | An enlargement of a shaft that affords room for landing at any desired place, and at the same time provides space for receiving loaded mine cars. Equipment and material to be used in the mine are taken from the cage at this place. Pumphouses to remove mine water are generally near the shaft stations. |
| **Sink-float:** | A heavy media separation process whereby crushed crude ore is introduce into a media, the specific gravity of which is between that of iron mineral and the worthless material. The iron sinks and the waste floats, effecting the desired separation. |
| **Skip:** | A large hoisting bucket, which slides between guides in a shaft, with handle or bail usually connecting at or near the bottom of the bucket so that it may be automatically dumped at the surface. *Note: In inclined shafts both cages and skips have wheels that run on rails throughout the shaft.* |
| **Slices:** | Drifts or cross-cuts driven off the sub level into the ore body. |
| **Sprag:** | A wooden prop for supporting timber sets, bearing pieces, equipment. |
| **Stockpile:** | A place where ore is accumulated at the surface when shipping is suspended. |
| **Stope:** | Underground void created by the extraction of ore. |
| **Stoper:** | A pneumatic drill for working stopes, raises, and narrow places. |
| **Sub level:** | Drifts or cross-cuts driven off of raises at intervals between main levels. |
| **Sump:** | An excavation to collect mine water for discharge to surface. |
| **Tamping:** | The process of stemming or filling a bore hole with inert materials. |
| **Timbering:** | A method of supporting an excavation by use of timber posts and cap, laced with lagging or cribbing. |
| **Timber field:** | An area adjacent to the shaft in which timber and supplies are stored. |
| **Transfer sub:** | A sub-level in which ore is mucked from the place it was mined to loading point. |
| **Travel road:** | An underground passage or way in which men travel to and from their working place. |
| **Ventilation:** | The method of producing, distributing, maintaining, conducting, and regulating constant current or flow of atmospheric air in mine shafts, levels, inclines and working places. Natural ventilation, fans, regulators and tubing, are combined to ventilate a mine. |
| **Water Leyner:** | A heavy duty pneumatic drill used to bore holes in rock. |

# SKETCH OF CROSS SECTION OF A MINE

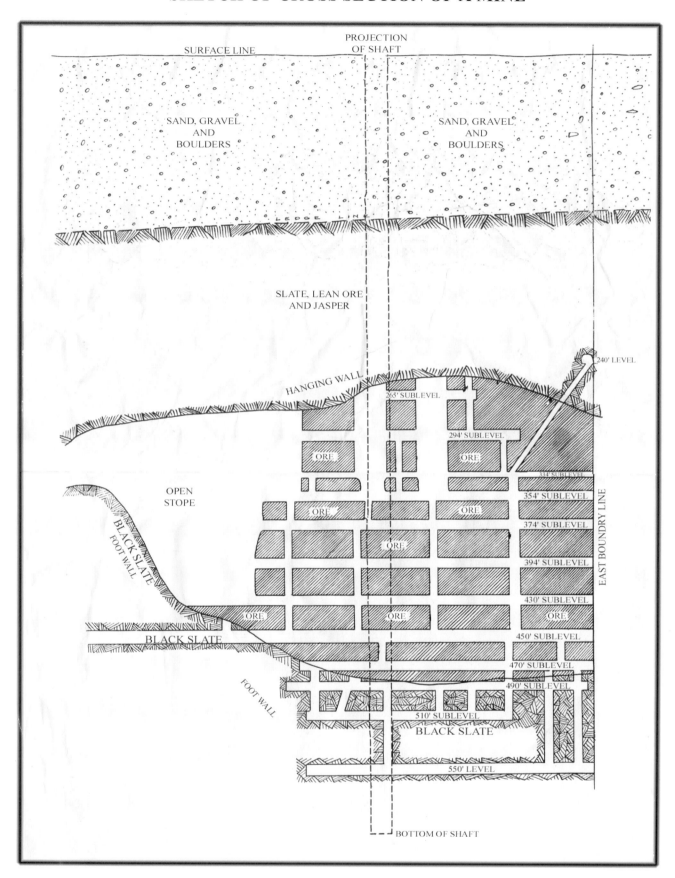

# MAP OF IRON COUNTY

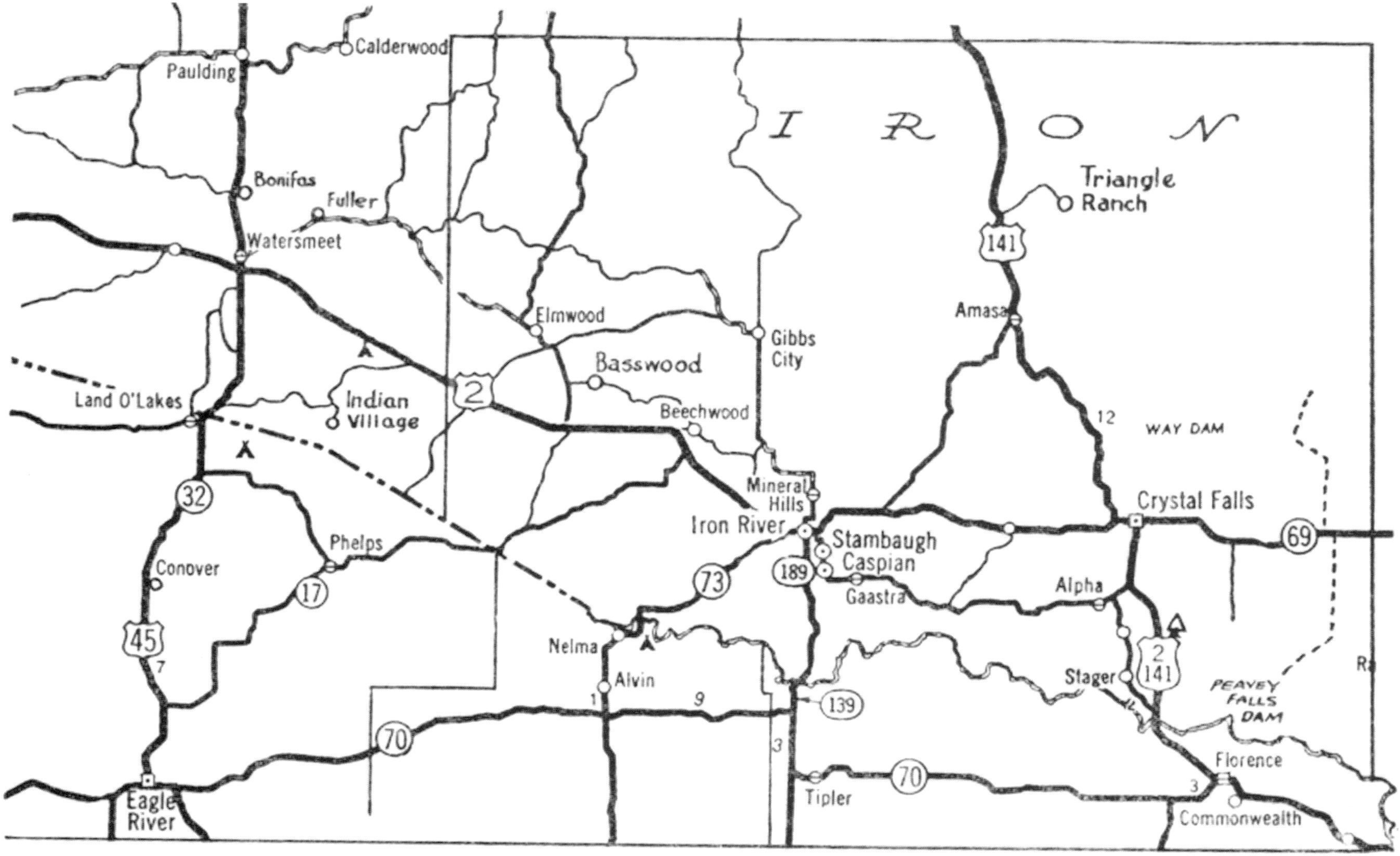

## ABOUT THE AUTHORS

Harold and Marcia Bernhardt are two of several founders of the Iron County Historical Museum Society, founded in 1962. Before retirement, both were high school teachers—Harold, history and Marcia, English. Harold served as President of the Society for 33 years, Marcia as curator of the Iron County Museum for as many years.

Harold for the most part, provided leadership to enlarge the Museum from one building to twenty-two. Active with the Chamber of Commerce, he received the prestigious designation as Ambassador of Michigan from the governor of the State, as well as other awards.

Marcia designed exhibits, worked with photographic preservation and researched and/or edited a dozen publications. She has been given the Athena Award for community service and was named writer of the year in 1992 by the Upper Peninsula of Michigan Writers' Association. Both Marcia and Harold were given the Charles Follo Award, in 1980 by the Historical Society of Michigan. They also received the cherished commendation for historical preservation from the American Association of State and Local History and the U.P. Gold Award for their contributions to Upper Peninsula tourism in 1999.

In 1999 they produced the book Barns, Farms and Yarns, a book of interviews on Iron County farming illustrated with 323 photographs of Iron County Barns.

Debra Bernhardt PHD, (1953-2001) their daughter, produced much of the basis for this publication, having interviewed over 115 people in the mining industry or related to it for a reading play entitled Black Rock and Roses, her undergraduate thesis at the University of Michigan. The author of many articles and several books, she served as Head Archivist at New York University from 1991 until her recent death. In the year 2000, she co-authored Ordinary People, Extraordinary Lives, a book of interviews and photographs of New York workers. She had planned to work with her parents on this publication.